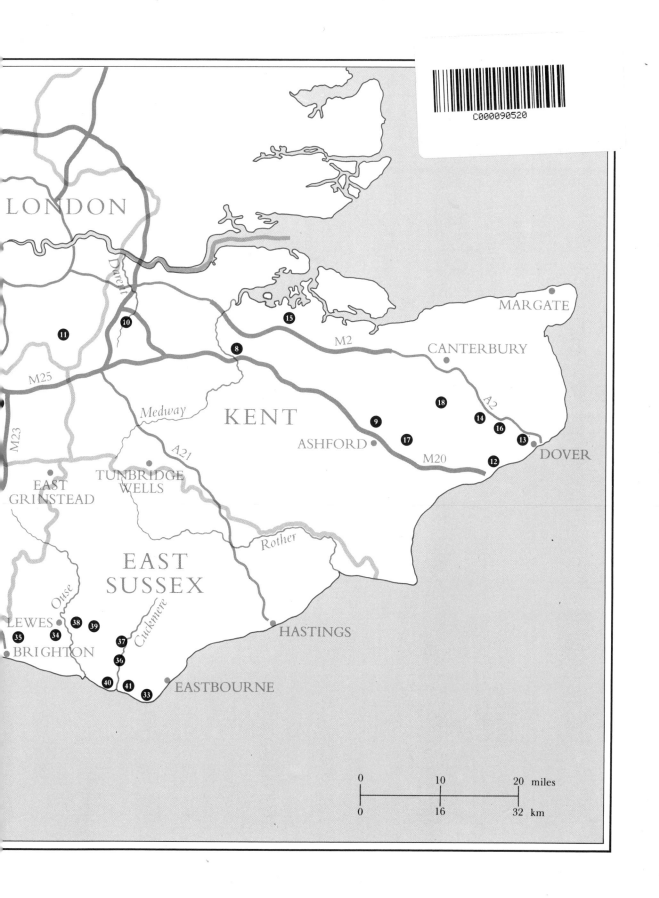

LONDON

MARGATE

CANTERBURY

KENT

Medway

M2

M25

M23

ASHFORD

Darent

A21

A2

EAST
GRINSTEAD

TUNBRIDGE
WELLS

DOVER

M20

Rother

EAST
SUSSEX

Ouse

Cuckmere

HASTINGS

LEWES

BRIGHTON

EASTBOURNE

⑪ ⑩ ⑧ ⑮ ⑱ ⑭ ⑯ ⑬ ⑨ ⑰ ⑫ ㉟ ㉞ ㊳ ㊴ ㊲ ㊱ ㊵ ㊶ ㉝

0		10		20	miles
0		16		32	km

DOWNLAND WILDLIFE

John Davis

Heyshott Down 6th July

DOWNLAND WILDLIFE

A Naturalist's Year in the North and South Downs

JOHN F. BURTON

JOHN DAVIS

GEORGE
PHILIP

First published in 1992 by George Philip Limited
59 Grosvenor Street, London W1X 9DA

British Library Cataloguing-in-Publication Data

Burton, John F.
  Downland Wildlife
  I. Title   II. Davis, John
  574.9422

ISBN 0–540–01259–9

Design Louise Dick
Page design Gwyn Lewis
Typeset by Keyspools Ltd, Golborne, Lancashire
Printed in Hong Kong

TITLE PAGE *Hobbies prey upon smaller
birds, such as larks, swallows and, as shown here,
house martins, as well as large flying insects.*

CONTENTS

Preface and
Acknowledgements
PAGE 6

The Region
PAGE 9

Spring
PAGE 33

Summer
PAGE 67

Autumn
PAGE 111

Winter
PAGE 139

Nature Reserves
and Areas of Interest
PAGE 170

Bibliography
PAGE 185

Index
PAGE 188

PREFACE AND
ACKNOWLEDGEMENTS

This book takes an exclusive and close look at the North and South Downs and the wildlife that inhabits them. I have attempted an ecological approach throughout, endeavouring to emphasize the inter-relationships between animal and plant communities. In many ways the seasonal format of the book has facilitated such an approach as well as, I hope, enabling the reader to plan his or her own excursions on the downs with a good idea of what to look for at a particular time of year. It is hoped, too, that the book will be helpful to the naturalist who already specializes in botany, ornithology or some other particular field, but wishes to extend his interests and knowledge into related branches of natural history.

Although specifically about the North and South Downs, much of what has been described and discussed in the book applies equally well to the calcareous downlands of the whole of England, including the older limestones of the West and Wales, and even those of Scotland and Ireland. I am, nevertheless, conscious of the many things that, for reasons of space, I have had perforce to leave out. This is particularly true of the invertebrates – so much greater in diversity of species and numbers than the plants, birds and mammals of southern England – and I have felt obliged to place the emphasis on those, especially the larger insects like butterflies, moths and grasshoppers, which are most likely to attract the notice of the rambler on the downs.

This brings to mind the need to state that, while this book has been written primarily for the layman and general reader rather than the experienced naturalist, every effort has been made to include up-to-date ecological information that will appeal to the latter. In this respect, I have read as widely as possible and am particularly grateful to the authors of publications listed in the Bibliography whose observations and studies have supplemented my own; any mistakes that the reader should find are solely mine; I would indeed be grateful if these are communicated to me, care of the publisher.

I have been fortunate that this book has been so beautifully illustrated by such a splendid wildlife artist as John Davis with whom I have greatly enjoyed working as well as sharing rewarding field excursions to the North and South Downs. John lives below the South Downs, near Chichester, and knows that wonderful, rolling range of hills well. He joins with me in warmly expressing our gratitude to those who have helped us in various ways: Michael Bright, R. M. Burton, Anne Griffiths (Environmental Officer, West Sussex), E. C. M. Haes, Carol Harries (Kent Trust for Nature Conservation), Graham Hart (British Butterfly

Conservation Society), K.H. Hyatt, Solene Morris (Curator, Charles Darwin Museum), Martin R. Newman (Surrey Wildlife Trust), D.F. Owen, Irene Palmer (Kent Trust for Nature Conservation) and Richard Tyler (Hampshire and Isle of Wight Wildlife Trust).

John Davis and I are also grateful to John Gaisford, Publishing Director (whose idea it was to write this book), Jo Hemmings, Natural History Editor, and Teresa Cockburn of George Philip Limited for their enthusiastic support and guidance; to Wega Schmidt-Thomée for her efficient and devoted typing of the manuscript and constructive criticism, and to Caroline Davis for her help in a variety of ways. John Davis would particularly like to thank Caroline for her faith and patience allowing him to spend such a wonderful time painting throughout the year.

Finally, a word of appreciation to everyone who reads this book: we hope that you will find as much pleasure as we do in roaming the downlands and observing their wildlife, and that you will join with us in supporting all those who are working hard to conserve them for us and future generations to continue to enjoy.

John F. Burton
November 1991

The roe buck's antlers reach their full growth for the rutting season in August, and are then lost in November or December.

April   John Davis

THE REGION

Foreigners are usually puzzled and amused to be told that the chalk hill ranges of England are called 'downs', when, in fact, they look as if they ought really to be called 'ups'. Actually, there is a perfectly logical explanation: a 'down' is derived from the Celtic word 'dun', which means a 'fort' or 'hill'. As is apparent from the various ancient hill forts situated on the summits of many a prominent down, in the region fort and hill were almost synonymous.

To those of us who know the downlands well, they have a special fascination: viewed from afar or below, the smooth roundness of their contours is pleasing to our eyes when compared with the admittedly more impressive, yet awesome jaggedness of most high mountain ranges. This is especially true of bare, unwooded downs like those at the eastern end of the South Downs, although these do not and have not appealed to everyone. In the eighteenth century Dr Samuel Johnson said of the downs around Brighton, 'that it is a country so truly desolate that if one had a mind to hang oneself at being obliged to live there, it would be difficult to find a tree on which to fasten a rope'.

Nevertheless, various other well-known writers, past and present, Richard Jefferies and W. H. Hudson among them, have enthused about the beauty and charm of the downs. In his *Nature in Downland* (1923), W. H. Hudson makes a perceptive observation when writing of the South Downs, 'On these downs, for the sight and the bodily sensation which cannot be dissociated from sight, there are no impossible chasms, no steep heights difficult to climb, nor jagged rocks and broken surfaces to impede free movement and passage.'

Blackthorn and cowslips are both typical spring downland plants.

The Stone Age people were attracted to the chalk downs by the local abundance of flints which they broke, chipped and flaked to make axe-heads, arrowheads and other simple tools for many thousands of years, right up to the beginning of the Bronze Age. The chalk ridges made natural walkways, and early man must have marvelled at the convenience they provided in otherwise largely inhospitable and hostile lowland country; and the way in which they led to the wide, open expanse of Salisbury Plain. No wonder that these ancient people attached mystical significance to the central chalk plain from which the trackways radiated and raised monuments like Avebury and Stonehenge there. This area was also the centre of the then small population of England.

Our distant ancestors of the Old, Middle and New Stone Ages, Bronze and Iron Ages, shunned the hidden and unknown dangers of the dense and impenetrable, oak-dominated woodlands that clothed the lowlands and the Weald, and sought the security of circular upland camps from which they could see most threats in good time and defend with confidence. The mainly beech woodlands of the then largely wooded, but relatively open, downs they found easier to penetrate because of the lack of undergrowth, and easier to clear with their primitive, and then increasingly sophisticated, tools as cultures progressed from the Old Stone Age to the Iron Age. The first farmers also found the dry, shallow and light, calcareous soils much easier to work than heavier clay, and their crops of barley and wheat grew particularly well on them. Moreover, as their cattle and sheep grazed the cleared areas, so the unique and characteristic downland turf developed.

The springiness of chalk down turf gives an effortless exhilaration to the stride. The reason for this springiness is that, for several inches below the surface, the well-drained soil is infiltrated by a dense mass of roots which binds it together and gives it elasticity. As well as the roots of numerous herbs and other plants of a great variety of species, there are the even more abundant roots of grasses like sheep's fescue, whose fine leaf blades form a level sward which rabbit and sheep grazing, where it occurs, keeps short. Most of these grasses and plants are perennial and persist year after year without depending upon the setting of seed. Grazing tends to be impartial and reduces competition between the different species by cropping all alike. From the aromatic herbs there arises a fragrance which is another of the delights of downland.

THE ATTRACTIONS OF DOWNLAND FOR THE NATURALIST

For a naturalist, particularly if one's interests lie in the fields of botany and entomology, the downs are really very special. There is a whole host of plants that grow especially well on chalky soil, many of them largely and others entirely confined to it, because of their specialized requirements. Also because of their close association with such chalk-loving plants, either as foodplants or in some other way, many insects and other invertebrates are likewise restricted to calcareous downland.

Birds, mammals and reptiles are not so specialized in their way of life that they are confined to chalk and limestone soils, but many species, nevertheless, find downland habitats well suited to them. However, apart from some of the river valleys which bisect the downs, the ornithologist generally finds less to interest him than the botanist and entomologist does. A perusal of the annually published local bird reports covering the North and South Downs reveals a marked tendency for bird-watchers to neglect the bird-life of the inland downs in favour of the coast and its cliffs, marshes and river estuaries because of their greater variety of species, especially at migration periods, and the likelihood of

seeing rarities. Yet there is still much to be seen and learned about the precise breeding and winter distributions of even common birds on the downs, to say nothing of the movement of migrants there.

Rooks bathing.

THE NORTH AND SOUTH DOWNS

The North and South Downs are two arms of the central high mass of chalk, centred on Salisbury Plain in Wiltshire, which extend octopus-like eastwards through Kent and Sussex to the English Channel. Another long and wide arm extends north-eastwards to the north Norfolk coast to form the Berkshire Downs, Chiltern Hills, Gog–Magog Hills and Breckland, in that order. Many of the eastern slopes of this ridge, which gradually flattens out to the north-east, are covered with glacial drift; those of Breckland are overlaid with sand which is so thin in places that the chalk is close to the surface. On the other side of the Wash, this arm of chalk reappears more impressively as the Lincolnshire and the Yorkshire Wolds, and swings north-west. South-westwards from Salisbury Plain a short arm extends almost to Bridport in the west of Dorset, with outliers around Beer and Branscombe in south Devon, and a narrow ridge stretching eastwards in the form of the Purbeck Hills and ending at Ballard Point, near Studland, Dorset. This narrow strip then reappears right across the Isle of Wight from west to east.

In the north-east corner of the central chalk mass, a ridge extends via the Newbury Downs – the highest chalk hills in Britain – and, after descending out of sight between Basingstoke and Farnham, rises again as a steep and narrow ridge, the Hog's Back, at the western end of the North Downs. Skirting the south bank of the Thames and its estuary, the North Downs ridge sweeps south-eastwards to meet the English Channel at the famous White Cliffs in the neighbourhood of Dover, Folkestone and South Foreland, Kent, with an outcrop in the shape of the Isle of Thanet between Margate and Ramsgate. Just to the north of the Thames there is an outcrop of the North Downs around Grays in Essex.

11

In the south-east corner of the central chalk mass a final, but shorter, arm than the North Downs extends east-south-eastwards to the sea at Beachy Head, near Eastbourne, Sussex, in the form of the South Downs. A southern outlier of the South Downs forms Portsdown, which rises steeply just north of Portsmouth. Since the North and South Downs are simply eastwards extensions of the central chalk mass, defining their actual beginnings is somewhat arbitrary. A more naturally obvious demarcation line for the start of the North Downs is the Hog's Back between Farnham and Guildford in Surrey, where the chalk ridge narrows to almost nothing at Farnham. In the case of the South Downs, however, the range is much wider where it extends east from just south of Petersfield and the western boundary is, therefore, less clear. Some maps, such as those produced by the Ordnance Survey, mark the North Downs as

Lullington Heath 4th October towards Friston Forest John Davis

extending almost as far west as Andover, Hampshire, and Newbury, Berkshire, where they merge with the high Newbury Downs. For the purpose of this book we have chosen to draw our western boundary for both the North and South Downs from the northern edge of the downs at Basingstoke, Hampshire, then south along the M3 motorway to Winchester; thence continuing due south along the course of the River Itchen to the southern edge of the downs around and above Twyford, a few miles north of Eastleigh and Southampton, in Hampshire. This boundary, therefore, includes a considerable part of the Hampshire Downs, and has the added advantage of including the village of Selborne, made famous by the parson-naturalist Gilbert White, whose renowned book *The Natural History of Selborne* (1789) and journals are of special interest. They contain his numerous observations of wildlife made in the

Ring ouzels on autumn passage from their breeding grounds in northern Europe to spend winter in southern Europe.

13

THE ZIG-ZAG AT SELBORNE

This path zig-zags up the very steep slope at the eastern end of Selborne Hanger, a magnificent example of a so-called 'hanging wood', so typical of the scarp slopes of chalk downland. The Zig-zag starts at the end of a footpath, an immemorial right of way from the village to the Hanger known as the 'Punfle', and was the idea of Gilbert White's younger brother John. He began digging it at the end of 1752, under Gilbert's direction and presumably, with his physical help as well. Its completion was eventually marked in 1768 by the placing at the summit of the Obelisk, now more popularly known as the Wishing Stone, a rough block of sandstone carted thence by Gilbert, John and their other brothers.

About two-thirds of the way up the Zig-zag, on the eastern side, there is the flat piece of ground where Gilbert White's Hermitage used to stand, a fanciful rustic hut with a domed, thatched roof. It was pulled down long ago. Here, he and his family and friends used to picnic in the summer and admire the wide panorama. This end of the Hanger used to be much more open in those days, with scrub rather than trees, so the views were much less interrupted than they are now, as contemporary drawings of 1776 show. Nowadays, one looks down the Zig-zag from the top through an avenue of tall beeches and other trees to a glimpse of the village 270 feet (*c*. 82 metres) below.

As one slowly climbs the Zig-zag in spring or early summer, the way is brightened with such wild flowers as red campion, yellow archangel, woodruff and hedge garlic, around which orange tip, holly blue and speckled wood butterflies disport. In the nearby trees and bushes great spotted and green woodpeckers, marsh tits, nuthatches, robins, lesser whitethroats, chiffchaffs, willow warblers and bullfinches are among the various birds that may be seen or heard. If one is lucky, the characteristic trills of the wood warbler and its less frequent piping song may be heard from the tall beeches of the adjacent Hanger. Gilbert White described it as a 'sibilous grasshopper-like noise' when he listened to it here and compared it with the songs of its close relatives, the willow warbler and the chiffchaff. He was the first person to distinguish between these three species, in 1768.

From the top of the Zig-zag there is access to a network of paths which traverse the plateau of the National Trust-managed Selborne Common and Hanger. A more or less open sheep down in White's day, Selborne Common is now a mixture of mature trees and scrub, interspersed with some open, grassy expanses, partly on the chalk itself and partly on an overlying bed of loamy brown clay with a few flints. The Common therefore supports an interesting and contrasting mixture of chalk-loving and calcifugous plants.

eighteenth century on the chalk downs above the village, as well as on the South Downs east to Ringmer, near Lewes, Sussex, during his regular journeys to visit his aunt there. Some authors, such as J. E. Lousley in his stimulating book *Wild Flowers of Chalk and Limestone* (1950), have treated Selborne as part of the North Downs, so we have an excellent precedent to follow.

THE GEOLOGY OF THE DOWNS: HOW THEY WERE FORMED

Before going on to describe the topography of the North and South Downs it is necessary to give some account of the basic geology and nature of chalk hills. It is important to remember that the chalk itself is largely formed from the fossilized remains of millions of sea creatures which lived and died in the seas where the calcareous mud accumulated.

Chalk is a limestone, but a softer and younger one than the oolitic limestones of the Cotswolds, which were deposited in the warm and humid Jurassic Period and largely consist of oolites – tiny fishroe-like spheres composed of minute shells of calcium carbonate massed together – and is much younger than the mountain limestones of western England that were formed in the tropical seas of the Carboniferous Period. It was, in fact, formed in the period following the Jurassic – the Cretaceous – a time, some 136 million years ago, when the north Atlantic Ocean opened up and most of northern Europe was covered by sea. It was in this sea that up to 600 metres (2000 ft) of chalk was laid down at the rate of about 10 cm (4 in) every 10,000 years. This soft, white, crumbly limestone weathers readily and is composed largely of microscopic spherical algae known as coccolithoporids, armoured with plates of calcium carbonate called coccoliths, as well as minute, often microscopic Foraminifera – marine Protozoan animals, which formed shells also of lime (calcium carbonate). In addition, the shells of other, larger marine animals that lived in this sea contributed to the formation of the calcium carbonate deposits that ac- cumulated on the sea floor. Like most other limestones, chalk was formed in a relatively shallow, calm, and clear sea; calmer than the strong tidal conditions in which oolitic limestone developed.

As well as the marine plants and animals whose limy plates and shells formed the chalk, there are layers of flints (fine crystalline quartz) believed to have been mainly derived from the skeletal remains of sponges protected with silica instead of calcium carbonate. These flints, black or brown in colour with white, chalky exteriors, are very hard and insoluble, and are often extremely numerous, especially in the upper regions of the chalk. In some places the chalk has been dissolved away, leaving the flint nodules as shingle beaches or river gravels. Such deposits therefore indicate where chalk once occurred, and where the flints are found on the downland tops, mixed with brown clay as 'clay- with-flints', the clay is derived from residues of later, superficial rocks which once overlaid the chalk.

Display-flighting at dusk and dawn during the breeding season – roding – is characteristic of male woodcocks.

The beds or layers of chalk are not uniformly pure and similar in composition; some are harder than others, particularly where flint strengthens them, while the lower ones can be soft, muddy and impure. About the end of the Cretaceous Period this process of chalk deposition in the sea came to an end when movements of the earth led to an uplifting of the sea bed and its chalk deposits. Almost the whole of Britain once again became dry land with the chalk left high and dry, like a vast white sheet extending over south-east England and adjacent parts of the Continent. Further uplifts occurred during the warm Tertiary Period, but there was also much weathering and denuding of the chalk when rivers, flowing down the sloping surface of the chalk to the sea, eroded much of it and exposed some of the older rocks underneath.

Then during the Miocene, about 25 million years ago, the folding of the Alps, due to the movements of the Earth's tectonic plates, reached their climax and the strong repercussions of this in Britain led to the folding of the chalk and other strata of south-east England. The vast chalk sheet and the strata of the Weald underneath were buckled up into a huge dome. This was exposed to the action of wind, rain and rivers, and gradually worn away, revealing the Wealden rocks beneath; these were eroded in turn, and of the chalk only the outer rims remained, and have since continued to be worn down. By the end of the Miocene Period, England had evolved the basic structure that we know today: its river systems and chalk escarpments were larger and more extensive, but essentially recognizable.

During the various glaciations of the Pleistocene Ice Ages, the ice never extended far enough south to cover the North and South Downs, which were therefore left free of the boulder clay deposited by the ice on the dip slopes of

17

the chalk hills north of the Thames. However, the normally porous chalk froze and did not allow melt-water to permeate it; thus during thaws in the glacial summer this surface water flowed off the downs in cascades, carrying with it much calcium carbonate in solution, and so speeding the erosion process and carving out valleys. In the Last Glaciation and for some time after it, southern England was still connected to the continental mainland because of the downward tilting of the land further north by the weight of the ice, and also because so much sea water was locked up in it, resulting in a marked lowering of the sea-level. Thus, until the final breaking of the land bridge at the beginning of the warm Atlantic Period, some 7000 years ago, plants and animals, including man, could move freely to and from the Continent. Moreover, until eroded away by the circulation of the sea between England and France, the chalk ridges of the North and South Downs were continuous with those of north-west France. Where the sea cut through, it left steep, almost vertical cliffs and headlands, because smooth chalk fractures along joint planes.

The chief reason why chalk still tends to occur as upland is that, because of its highly porous nature and lack of surface rivers and streams, it suffers relatively little from erosion from those sources in contrast to the adjacent clays. As pointed out by Sir Arthur Trueman in his classic and highly readable book *Geology and Scenery in England and Wales* (1949), 'the Chalk thus stands out in ridges as surely as if it were a harder rock'.

As Sir Arthur Trueman has also pointed out, there are generally few rivers in chalk country, but characteristically many dry valleys. That they remain dry is clearly due to the porosity of the chalk allowing rain water to seep immediately downwards; but this does not explain their origin. The presence of alluvial and gravel deposits at the bottoms of many of them indicates that these must have been carried down by rivers that once flowed through the valleys and created them. These rivers are believed to have flowed during times of heavier rainfall than nowadays and during the Ice Age when the chalk downs were frozen and the surface melt-water flowed off them in the summer thaws. A reason that has been advanced to explain why they subsequently dried out completely is that the gradual erosion of the clay vales and the chalk escarpment steadily lowered the water table of the saturated chalk so that it dropped below the valley floors on the downland dip slopes, thus causing the rivers or streams to vanish.

THE TOPOGRAPHY OF THE NORTH AND SOUTH DOWNS

Nowadays, most of the rivers and streams in the region covered by this book have their origin in the high ground of the Weald, between the North and South Downs, and cut through the chalk ridges on their way to the coast, having in the past made deep and impressive gaps in the downs. Particularly impressive are those carved by the rivers Great Stour, Medway, Darent, Mole and Wey in the North Downs and the Cuckmere, Ouse, Adur and Arun in the

South Downs. Some of the downland streams have their origin in the downs themselves – from springs situated at the base of the chalk where it rests on the narrow belt of upper greensand and the impermeable gault clay; these either flow into the Weald rivers that pass through the downland gaps or flow north or south, away from the chalk ridges.

Those rivers cutting through the North Downs flow into the London Basin to join the Thames on its journey to the North Sea. The thick layer of chalk which was folded upwards in a dome-like anticline over the Weald – now long since eroded away to reveal its remnant outer ridges (the North and South Downs) and the older rock strata of the Weald – dips deep down in a syncline under the London Basin and its famous river to reappear north-west of London as the Chiltern Hills. This chalk underlying the London Basin is covered with younger deposits, amongst which London clay is predominant.

The northern dip slope of the North Downs rises gently and gradually from the London Basin for several miles before reaching the crest of the very steep, south-facing scarp slope, some 183 metres (600 feet) or more above sea-level. This escarpment forms a much longer ridge than the South Downs, but does not quite attain for much of its length the average height of the latter, which rise to their highest point of 255 metres (836 feet) at Duncton Hill, with Linch Down, near Bepton, and Ditchling Beacon, both at 248 metres (813 feet), a close equal second. Nevertheless, much of the crest of the North Downs between the Rivers Wey and Medway exceeds 213 metres (700 feet), and at Botley Hill, Surrey, it attains 267 metres (875 feet), a greater height than anywhere on the South Downs. Betsom's Hill, near Westerham, Kent, is another high point on the North Downs at 251 metres (824 feet). At the western end of the North Downs, the so-called Hog's Back, the ridge between Farnham and Guildford is very narrow and relatively low at around 137 metres (450 feet), with the slopes on both sides equally steep. Downland escarpments are normally at their steepest and highest where the dip slope is very gradual and not steep; where the dip slope is steep, then the whole chalk outcrop is narrow, as at the Hog's Back. The impressively steep escarpments of both the North and South Downs proper, which face each other, are still being very slowly eroded by wind and rain; therefore both are steadily moving away northwards and southwards respectively.

Generally speaking, the scenery of the North Downs is more varied than that of the South Downs. The soil covering the steeper slopes and escarpments of both ranges is thin and very chalky; but on the more gentle dip slopes the chalk is overlaid, here and there, with large deposits of clay, gravel or sand from relatively recent times, such as the Eocene Period (about 50 million years ago) or subsequently. Much of this is neutral or acidic and carries a distinctly different flora from neighbouring chalky areas. In places on the North Downs there are large areas of clay-with-flints, especially on the plateau-like tops. This distinctive residue is most readily seen in the large ploughed fields where the flints lie scattered about in the reddish-brown loamy clay. The tops of the South Downs, in contrast, tend to be covered with a thin layer of loam.

Broad-leaved woodland, especially of beech, grows particularly well on the clay-with-flints, and, on the whole, the North Downs are more heavily wooded and less open in character than the South Downs. Oak, sweet chestnut and hornbeam are other broad-leaved trees which grow well on this soil on the North Downs and also, with birch, larch and Scots pine, where the soil is pebbly or sandy. There are few woods of any size on the South Downs east of the River Arun, apart from Friston Forest, just east of the Cuckmere, which has largely been planted by the Forestry Commission, and on the dip slopes between Arundel and Worthing. Westwards of the Arun, as far as the A3 road between Petersfield and Portsmouth, the woods are much more extensive, with beech again the dominant tree species.

Sheep-farming is much less important on the South Downs than it used to be when W. H. Hudson wrote *Wildlife in Downland* (1923), but is still carried on, especially in the more open eastern sectors; and there are some signs of local revival, notably in the interests of nature conservation. Many of the former sheep downs have been ploughed up this century in favour of arable farming, especially cereal production. Some downland fields that used to be lilac or purple-blue with lucerne are now pale blue with linseed flax crops, while others are bright yellow in late spring with the currently popular oilseed rape, usually grown as a break crop. Root crops of various kinds, beans and maize are also grown in these downland fields which are often of huge size and unseparated by hedgerows; instead, barbed wire is preferred. Much of this is also true of the

The marbled white butterfly is common on the South Downs from late June until August.

North Downs, although sheep-farming was less important. Here, as on the South Downs, grazing cattle are more commonly seen nowadays, especially Friesians. Sadly, old-fashioned oast-houses and orchards are not as familiar a sight as they used to be on the slopes of the North Downs in Kent: the oast-houses have mainly been converted into fashionable houses, while the mechanically collected hops are dried out in ordinary-looking barns; and the old orchards have been replaced with modern, clinical-looking orchards of small trees, producing a limited number of apple varieties compared to former times. The return of vineyards to the slopes of the North and South Downs, once common in medieval times, is a new development since about 1970.

Most of the North Downs as far west as Farnham and the whole of the South Downs from Eastbourne to Winchester are protected as Areas of Outstanding Natural Beauty (AONBs). There are many magnificent views along the escarpments and hilltops of these two downland ranges, and most of these can be enjoyed by walkers, cyclists and horse-riders who use the recently opened South Downs Way (1972) and North Downs Way (1978). The first-named extends for more than 100 miles (160 km) from Eastbourne to Winchester, and the latter for 141 miles (227 km) from Dover to Farnham. Both follow ancient ridgeways for long distances, including, on the North Downs, the medieval Pilgrims' Way. More details are given under 'Nature Reserves'.

Dark green fritillary at Folkestone Warren with peregrine falcon and gulls in the background.

RED-LEGGED AND GREY PARTRIDGES

These studies of red-legged and grey partridges and lapwings resting in stubble fields in late summer give some idea of how well camouflaged they are in this phase of their daily cycle, when they are particularly vulnerable to attack from large birds of prey or ground predators. Look at red-legged partridges, for example, away from their natural habitat, such as stuffed ones in a museum, and they will appear conspicuous because of their white eye stripes and white throats bordered by a jet black band and marginal spots, bright red bills and legs, and flanks boldly barred with red, black and white on lavender-blue. But in their normal habitats, like this field, such bright, bold markings and colours break up their outlines so that they merge with the light and shade of their background: the stripes harmonize with the grass and straw stems and plant leaves; the white faces become sun-bleached stones contrasting with dark shadow; the bright red bills become scarlet flowers, poppies, perhaps; while their dark brown backs resemble clods of earth. The duller, though handsome, grey partridges look even more like clods of earth among a scattering of grass stalks. And so do these relaxing lapwings: yet their black and white plumage is so striking when they stand up or fly, their mantles glowing an iridescent green in the sunshine. Again their pied plumage breaks up their outline into light and shade, and their dark mantles look earth-like and so act as camouflage.

Lapwings nest here and there in downland fields, before the crops have grown high. Not only are the adults well camouflaged when sitting on their nests, a scrape in the ground with a little grass lining, but the eggs and chicks are so camouflaged in khaki with black markings that they are almost invisible.

As can be imagined, grey and red-legged partridges are also extremely difficult to see when sitting on their nests, which are cunningly concealed in the tangled vegetation in hedge-bottoms, wood borders or similar situations. Their eggs are not so well camouflaged; those of the grey, being olive-brown in colour, are more effective, however, than the pale yellowish-brown, red-speckled eggs of the red-leg. Grey and red-leg chicks, which also have patterns which blend well with their surroundings, leave the nest soon after hatching and feed in the company of their parents until the family covey joins up with others.

Often, the first sight one has of either partridge species is when a pair or covey (small flock) suddenly rises from the ground at one's approach, and rockets off down the hillside with a loud explosion of flurrying wings and harsh alarm calls, skimming low over obstacles on down-curved wings to land some distance away. Red-legs, however, tend to run for a considerable distance before flying and are more inclined to disperse. Both species form their coveys in late summer, after breeding has finished, and they stay together until next spring.

Resting under hedge August 24th.
stubble, chalk & flints.

2nd September
in burnt stubble

Lapwings in newly cut RAPE August 30th.

Early morning.
light through mists.

John Davis

The ecology of the chalk

Just as there is a strong connection between the type of vegetation growing in an area and its geology, so there is a close association between the vegetation and the animal communities found in a habitat, especially the insects. This book follows J. E. Lousley's straightforward classification of plant communities on the chalk soils of Box Hill, Surrey, as used in his admirable book *Wild Flowers of Chalk and Limestone* (1950), which can be applied generally over the region as a whole. These are: (a) chalk grassland; (b) chalk scrub; (c) woodland.

Chalk grassland

The delightfully springy turf that characterizes chalk downland has already been mentioned. A major problem facing plants growing on the dry chalk of the North and South Downs is that of obtaining sufficient water and withstanding drought. The very porous chalk is capable of holding a great deal of water before it becomes saturated, but this soon percolates down to much lower levels and, in the absence of more rain, the chalk soon dries out. Plants growing in the thin soil above are subject to strong drying winds which also cause surface water to evaporate rapidly. Therefore the grasses and plants forming the turf have had to evolve such means of avoiding moisture loss through transpiration as reducing their height; folding or rolling their leaves, as in some grasses; developing small leaves, long hairs and thick cuticles; and by flowering early to avoid the normally dry period of high summer. Some plants, like common rock-rose, horseshoe vetch, salad burnet and wild thyme send down long roots through the massed roots of the grasses and smaller plants and deep into the chalk to reach any water held there; those of horseshoe vetch have been known to reach 90 cm (36 in). Naturally, the competition for water is intense: most plants are therefore long-living perennials, some of them spreading vegetatively, thereby leaving less space for new plants growing from seed to establish themselves. Where the turf is continuous it is more effective in conserving moisture. Some grasses and other flowering plants are specially adapted to calcareous soils and rarely grow elsewhere.

The steeper the slope the more quickly rainwater is lost and leached soil carried away, so the steep escarpment slopes have a higher calcium carbonate content than the lower, gentler ones. A sharply angled slope has little ability to hold soil and is therefore often bare or sparsely vegetated. An angle greater than 38 degrees, for instance, is unable to support closely grazed grassland.

Thin soils with short vegetation warm up quickly in the sunshine, especially those on south-facing slopes. This is an important factor in the ecological requirements of many insects, including some beetles, butterflies and grasshoppers which are largely or entirely restricted in their distribution to south-facing calcareous slopes. Some of them are there because they need the sunshine and heat to complete their life cycles successfully; and others, for instance butterflies like the adonis and chalk-hill blues, because their particular larval foodplants grow best in such situations.

The hobby, a summer visitor, is a predator of dragonflies.

Many such insect species, characteristic of calcareous grasslands, disappear when scrub and, finally, woodland invades their specialized habitat. One wonders how common and widespread they were in prehistoric times before the well-wooded downlands were cleared by man. Presumably, populations of them existed in such areas or patches of open grassland as existed, mainly on the steeper or seaward slopes; if an area gradually became overgrown with scrub and unsuitable they were perhaps able to disperse short distances along grassy corridors to the next nearby open and suitable site. Even on grassland sites which were extensive in historical times, most, if not all, of these species, such as the blue butterflies, often do not occupy all of the habitat, but form discrete colonies. Perhaps this habit is an adaptation to primeval conditions when much of England, including the downlands, was covered with thick woodland, and areas of grassland were fragmented and not extensive. It seems probable that these grassland species were not as widespread as in comparatively recent historical times.

Insects and other invertebrates provide food for spiders and predatory insects like robber flies, ground beetles and hunting wasps, as well as for amphibians, lizards, some mammals and many species of birds. Some of those invertebrate predators typically found in chalk grassland, which may be mentioned here, are the common toad, common lizard, common and pygmy shrew, mole, hedgehog, red-legged partridge, stone curlew, green woodpecker, swallow, skylark, meadow pipit, grasshopper-warbler, stonechat, whinchat, wheatear, corn bunting, yellowhammer, starling and jackdaw.

The foliage of grasses and other vegetation is eaten by a wide variety of herbivorous insects, of which grasshoppers and Lepidoptera are particularly

27

Darwins Orchid Bank, 4 Ju

important, and such mammals as hares, rabbits and voles, as well as domesticated cattle and sheep. With the exception of the last two (although some new-born lambs may be taken by foxes), these, in turn, or their young will be preyed upon by foxes, stoats, weasels, buzzards, hen harriers, kestrels, little and short-eared owls, carrion crows, adders and other predators. Sparrow hawks and, in winter, merlins hunt smaller birds on the wing, such as thrushes, finches and sparrows, which flock to feed on the seeds of fruits of many of the downland plants and shrubs in late summer or autumn.

CHALK SCRUB

Open chalk grassland is subject to invasion by scrub and there are, in fact, few expanses in which scattered shrubs have not become established. Where grazing by herbivorous mammals, like rabbits and sheep, is intense, shrubs will be held in check. When grazing is relaxed or removed, these shrubs, which may be quite old, even though small, will begin to increase in size and will eventually grow large enough to shade out the herbaceous plants; seedlings from them will also become established and grow, and will be joined by the seedlings of other invading scrub species. Eventually, if still unchecked, some of the shrub species, like hawthorn and spindle, will develop into small trees. By this time, the seedlings of beech, field maple and other trees growing on calcareous soils will also have begun to colonize the former open grassland and the vegetational climax of mature woodland will be well on its way to formation. Thus scrub is an intermediate stage in the transformation of grassland to woodland and merges one into the other.

The most typical of the downland shrubs and their associated insect fauna are discussed in the spring and summer chapters, where information on the breeding birds and mammals characteristic of the chalk scrub will also be found. The berries and fruits that the shrubs bear in autumn and accounts of some of the animals that feed on them, are described in the autumn chapter. However, it should be mentioned here that since scrub is an intermediate stage in the switch from grassland to woodland, the flora and fauna obviously vary as the changes gradually take place. Typical grassland wild flowers, such as horseshoe and kidney vetches, birds-foot trefoil, eyebright, marjoram, small scabious, burnet-saxifrage, hairy violet and fragrant orchid, linger on until the shade becomes too dark; so, too, will some grassland butterflies – chalk-hill and common blues, brown arguses, small heaths and meadow browns – as long as sufficient quantities of their larval foodplants and nectaring flowers survive. Meanwhile, they will be gradually replaced by brimstones, green hairstreaks, ringlets, speckled woods and other species of scrub and woodland edge, the two groups of species overlapping for a considerable time. Plants of woodland edge which can tolerate a large degree of shading, including hoary ragwort, bugle, ploughman's spikenard, and fly and man orchids will prosper until it becomes too dark for them. Likewise, the bird-life will gradually change from those species typical of grassland (for example, meadow pipit and skylark) to those who colonize scrubland at an early stage of development (such as grasshopper-

Darwin's Orchid Bank has many typical orchids of the region including the twayblade, fragrant, pyramidal and common spotted.

29

warbler, tree-pipit and whinchat); then to those who come in at a later stage (linnet, whitethroat and yellowhammer); followed, finally, by those that are most characteristic of woodland edge (bullfinch, nightingale, willow warbler, garden warbler, turtle dove and sparrow hawk).

WOODLAND

The most widespread and characteristic woodland of southern chalk downland has beech as the dominant species of tree; however, in some places the evergreen box and yew form woods with so dense a canopy that they are the only species present, except perhaps at the edges or where they thin out. The broad-leaved, deciduous beech woods also frequently develop a closed canopy that permits too little light to allow all but a few specialized plant species to grow underneath. The comparative dryness of the woodland floor is, moreover, another important factor which contributes to this lack of a shrub or herb layer, particularly on the porous chalk downs. Some of the plants which have, nevertheless, become adapted to live under the beech wood canopy include spurge-laurel and stinking hellebore, and the saprophytes yellow bird's-nest and bird's-nest orchid. The last two lack green leaves and cannot therefore photosynthesize; they obtain their nourishment instead from the masses of dead and decaying leaves on the woodland floor. Woods of beech, box and yew all become the climax of the vegetational succession where they develop on chalk.

On the flattish tops of the downs where the chalk is overlaid with the clay-with-flints deposits and their deeper, loamy soil, beech wood also develops as climax woodland. This is usually referred to as 'plateau type' beech wood by ecologists in contrast to the 'escarpment type' which grows on the shallow soils of pure chalk, often on the slopes and forming 'hanging' woods or 'hangers', like the famous Selborne Hanger, near Alton, in north-east Hampshire. These plateau beech woods are usually less pure stands of beech than the 'escarpment type', and contain a lot of common (pedunculate) oak (often sub-dominant) and a good variety of other trees, including box, yew and Scots pine, especially towards the margins. Many of these trees, notably the beeches, oaks, box and yew grow taller than on the chalk. As the leaf canopy tends also to be more open, there is usually a well-developed shrub layer of bracken, brambles, elder, hazel, holly and honeysuckle. The herb layer is often well developed as well, with such flowering plants as bluebell, dog's mercury, sanicle, woodruff and wood sorrel. As these woods are damper than the escarpment type and the thick soil is rich in humus, the soil may become acidic, thus encouraging the growth of a flora that contrasts with that of the woods on the strongly calcareous soils.

Some of the insects and other invertebrates living in the clay-with-flints woodland may be rare or absent in the chalk woodland, and vice versa. On the other hand, many species are less exacting in their ecological needs and will be found in woods of both types. For instance, moths like the barred hook-tip, August thorn, lobster moth, barred sallow and green silver-lines will inhabit both as long as their larval foodtrees, which include beech, are present. The orange footman is an example of a moth which is more frequently met with in the mature woods on the clay-with-flints. Its caterpillars feed only on lichens growing mainly on beech and oak trees: it occurs on both the North and South Downs, but seems to have disappeared from many localities since 1960.

The bird-life of the downland woods tends to be less affected by the nature of the soil. Nevertheless, the absence or lack of secondary vegetation in the chalk beech woods limits the nesting sites available to many species such as blackcaps, and they are more at home in the plateau-type woods on clay-with-flints. Robins, which obtain a lot of their invertebrate food amongst the leaf litter, are happy in both types of woodland so long as there is some nesting cover, and so are the canopy-feeding, ground-nesting wood warblers. Hole-nesters and canopy-feeders, like nuthatches and tits, do almost as well in the chalk woods, provided there are enough natural holes in the trees or nest boxes are available, while the completely arboreal woodpeckers are more or less equally at home in both types. Unlike the great and lesser spotted woodpeckers, the green woodpecker spends much time feeding on ants on the ground, and is therefore particularly well suited to the escarpment-type chalk woods which are within easy reach of the ant-hills of the yellow meadow ant amongst the scrub and on the open grassland of the downland slopes. Here and there in the broad-leaved woods of the North and South Downs of whatever type, so long as there is a minimum of cover, a few pairs of woodcocks nest amongst the leaf-litter, relying on their marvellous camouflage to escape detection. At night, tawny owls seek wood mice and other small rodents in all the downland woods, provided there are enough large holes or cavities in which to breed. As they glide through the trees they may well encounter badgers foraging below.

The long-eared owl nests in small numbers throughout the downland woods and plantations, especially in conifers.

31

SPRING

It is a joy to look for the first early signs of spring; yet they may already be searched for early in January. Many plants of early spring push their leaves above ground at this time: dog's mercury, wild arum, coltsfoot, sweet violet, primrose and lesser celandine, to name but a few. Some, like the stinking hellebore, a local plant of the downland woods, will even begin to flower in January and February.

So it is not easy to define precisely when spring begins: in fact, it is a gradual, imprecise process. Not all birds wait until spring has obviously arrived before they start nesting operations. Rooks may begin in February and mild weather in the first two months of the year can even induce April nesters like blackbirds, song thrushes and robins to lay eggs, although such early nests usually come to grief if cold weather suddenly returns.

Certain species of moths appear very early in the new year. For instance, the appropriately named early moth emerges in the downland hedgerows and wood borders on mild days in January and February. Other early species include the spring usher, one of the first moths, as its name implies, to usher in spring – as early as the middle of February; the pale brindled beauty also appears about the same time, but in mild weather can emerge from its underground pupae as early as January; the dotted border, the small brindled beauty and the day-flying (in sunshine) orange underwing. True to its name, the March moth does not normally appear on the wing before that month, when, like the others, it can frequently be discovered during the daytime, resting on tree-trunks or wooden fences. After dark, the males take flight and are often attracted towards artificial light.

Like all the species just mentioned, the March moth belongs to the large Geometer family of moths (Geometridae), so called because of the manner in which the caterpillars seem to be measuring their own length as they walk, arching their bodies in a characteristic way. Also like these species, with the exception of the orange underwing, the females are wingless or almost so.

As well as Geometers, some of the Noctuid moths are also harbingers of spring. Among these are the attractively named early grey, yellow horned, powdered quaker, twin-spotted quaker, small quaker, hebrew character and red chestnut. All of them will have over-wintered in the pupal stage, mostly in

A badger sow and her two cubs emerging from the sett in early June.

33

underground cells, and have been stimulated to emerge by the arrival of mild weather. Often a cold spell in February or March will hold up the emergence of early spring moths. Consequently, the sudden arrival of high temperatures at the abrupt end of such a cold spell often leads to a mass emergence of several species; then they will be seen resting in large numbers on woodland trees in the daytime, or, at night, the headlights of a car driven along a woodland road will reveal their ghostly forms flying in large numbers.

SALLOW BLOSSOM

Among them, from late February onwards, will be certain species of moth that went into hibernation in the adult form last autumn and have now been tempted forth by rising temperatures. They include the chestnut, the satellite, grey shoulder-knot, the herald and tawny pinion. All of them are widespread and common in and around the woods of the North and South Downs. Unlike the Geometer moths, these Noctuids or, as they are sometimes called, owlet moths, are in need of sustenance after their long winter sleep. The most prolific sources of energy-providing nectar are the golden-yellow sallow catkins which are so plentiful in the downland woods and hedgerows. On these sweet-smelling blossoms the moths often jostle with each other at dusk and after dark to suck the life-giving fluid, quite frequently becoming intoxicated and drowsy from it. Many fall prey to pipistrelle and other small bats which circle the sallow bushes and seize them as they approach or fly away.

In daytime, sallow blossom attracts many day-flying insects: bees, wasps and butterflies just out of hibernation, such as brimstones, commas, peacocks and small tortoiseshells. Apart from the nectar of their catkins, the sallows are a valuable resource for wildlife. Members of the willow family of trees, their foliage provides food for a wide range of insects, especially the caterpillars of Lepidoptera. Among these are the sallow kitten, puss moth, eyed and poplar hawk-moths, and the now rare and local purple emperor butterfly. The commonest British species of sallow is the goat willow, otherwise known as great sallow or pussy willow, and is the one usually to be found growing on the downs, most frequently in or near woods. The popular name pussy willow is due to the smooth, silky, kitten-like feel of the female catkins which grow on separate trees to those bearing the male catkins. The beautiful, golden-yellow male catkins are employed in the decoration of churches on Palm Sunday (the Sunday before Easter) and are therefore known as 'palm'.

BIRTH OF BADGER CUBS

Badger sows will be delivering their litters of up to five cubs (two or three is the usual number) deep in the underground security of a nursery chamber in the colony's sett, surrounded by the musky warmth of a thick bedding of hay and

34

bracken, at any time between the middle of January and the middle of March, but February is the peak time on the downs of south-east England. The cubs are blind and helpless at birth, and mainly pink in colour with only a sparse covering of silver hair, plus some black hairs on their paws and, where the black stripes will develop on their faces. Five weeks will elapse before their eyes open, but in another three weeks or so, usually about the end of March, they will have grown big enough to begin venturing above ground, even though they have yet to be weaned. Their mother feeds them with her milk several times a day before, about three months after birth, she starts to wean them on semi-digested food, especially worms, which she regurgitates to them.

Weaning generally occurs in May, a time when food is becoming plentiful. However, drought at this period may lead to the death of many cubs. Even in normal conditions, it has been estimated that, on average, more than a third of all cubs will die before they are old enough to leave the sett and forage with the adults. Moreover, over half of them are doomed to die before they reach their first birthday, two-thirds of them males. When the sow is foraging, some of these young cubs may be found in their underground nurseries by stoats or terriers and carried off and killed, although there are few direct observations of this.

Although the cubs only weigh about 100 g (3½ oz) when they are born, by the time the sow starts to wean them they are likely to weigh more than a kilo (2 lbs). By this stage in mid–May they will have been appearing regularly at the entrances to the sett around dusk. As they gradually learn to take solid food, such as beetles and worms, they steadily increase in weight and may attain a weight of 3 kg (6½ lbs) at the age of four months. By this time they are learning to find their own food and begin foraging with their mother. At six months of age they may weigh 6 kg (13 lbs). They still continue to live with their mother, and will do so until the autumn at least and perhaps through their first winter too. When, and if, they reach their first birthday they may well weigh as much as 9 kg (almost 20 lbs).

On the downlands of southern England, female badger cubs normally mature by the time they are a year old or shortly afterwards. Males, however, take about two years to do so. As soon as they are mature, both sexes begin mating and will do so throughout the year, although the peak period is from February to May, when fertilization takes place. This is a period of great and noisy activity, and one of the best times for the badger-watcher. Older sows will, of course, have already deposited their cubs by this time, but although they may be fertilized by the boar (male), owing to the Mustelid (weasel family) phenomenon of delayed implantation, they will not give birth to their next cubs until early the following spring. The fertilized eggs, or blastocysts, are retained in the uterus in a state of suspended development and do not become implanted in the uterine wall until about the end of December at which time the foetuses start their development. This presence of undeveloped blastocysts in the sow's uterus does not prevent further oestrus cycles occurring. Thus delayed implantation allows maximum opportunities for mating and ensures that the cubs are born at the best time for suckling them successfully.

SPRING DIARY

As well as the unscented common dog violets and wood dog violets of the more open downland woods and scrub, the only British violet with scented flowers, the sweet violet, is also particularly addicted to calcareous soils. It is also more tolerant of shady conditions and is therefore one of the few plants which can grow (see picture) in the deep shade of the beech woods, provided the canopy does not shut out too much light. For that reason, like other wild flowers of the beech woods, it starts blossoming early, often in February, before the beech foliage becomes too dense; by May its flowers are over. Sweet violets will also be found growing in the rather less shady conditions of wood borders and hedgebanks. Their flowers are usually violet, but may often be white. Their fragrance is sufficient to identify them from other violets, but their rounder, shinier and almost hairless leaves help too.

The wheatear is one of the earliest of the summer migrant birds to arrive on the south coast, often early in March. However, the main northward passage takes place in April, and John Davis painted the male at the top right of the page, with a cowslip in the background, just as the migration was passing its peak. Very few pairs remain to breed on the South Downs as they still used to do in the 1890s when W. H. Hudson wrote about them; but around a dozen pairs nest nowadays on the coast at Rye Harbour, halfway between the eastern extremities of the North and South Downs.

May, when John Davis painted this portrait of a nightingale in full song (centre right), is the best month to listen out for this rightly famous songbird. To hear it in the silence of night, echoed perhaps by a neighbouring, rival male, is to hear it at its best. But the nightingale sings freely in the daytime too, although its voice tends to be drowned by a medley of powerful songs from blackcaps, garden warblers and other songbirds. Moreover, one has a good chance of seeing it in daylight, but it requires the patience of our artist as it is a secretive species, and it may be necessary to sit quietly for a long while before it reveals itself as clearly as does the bird in the picture.

By the time the carpets of bluebells are coming into full flower in the downland oak and hazel woods, the hazels are in full leaf and the nightingales in full song – and such a hazel copse as the one depicted on the adjacent plate is a good breeding habitat for nightingales. Their nests are generally hard to find though, as they are usually well hidden on or a little above the ground amongst the bluebells, or in nettle patches or other dense vegetation.

APRIL 6th
Sweet violets
under old beech.

John Davis
Haslett Copse   May 4th

Badgers are to be found everywhere on the North and South Downs, and in some wooded areas are numerous, especially on the North Downs, including areas close to London. Unfortunately, they will most often be seen by the casual observer as road casualties on the roads of the region, especially the fast ones. Many of these are young boars seeking new territory and therefore unfamiliar with such hazards in new areas into which they wander. A welcome development in the construction of some new roads is the provision of underpasses where well-used badger paths are known to cross them. This, at least, has the effect of reducing badger road casualties.

FLOWERS OF EARLY SPRING

Intensive farming long ago destroyed much of the former open downland turf around Cissbury Hill, near Steyning in West Sussex, as it has in many other parts of the South Downs, and, indeed, the North Downs too. But in early spring the hedgerows and those rough corners of the cultivated downs which have escaped the plough will become bright with a variety of early spring flowers in common with the unspoilt coombes and slopes of the uncultivated stretches. Some of these plants will have emerged above ground early in January and by late February will already have begun to blossom: coltsfoot, dandelion, dog's mercury, field speedwell, lesser celandine and red deadnettle among them.

Dog's mercury, a low dark-green herb of deeply shaded woodlands, continues to flower far into May and is one of the few plants which thrives in the beech woods. It spreads by means of creeping rhizomes, often carpeting the ground. The male and female flowers are found on separate plants; those of the male are greenish and are borne on long, conspicuous spikes. The pollen from these male flowers is blown far and wide by the often cold winds of early spring. The female flowers are fewer and less conspicuous. Dog's mercury is poisonous and has an unpleasant smell which warns grazing animals to avoid it.

Two other plants which produce green flowers early in the spring, but which are special to chalk and limestone hills, are stinking hellebore and spurge-laurel. Both sometimes bloom as early as January or February and are in full flower by early March; both may be seen in the famous beech hanger at Selborne, Hampshire. By the middle of April the handsome purple-edged, yellow-green flowers of the hellebore and the small greenish ones of the spurge-laurel are past their best. As its name indicates, in contrast to the sweet-scented, insect-pollinated flowers of the spurge-laurel, the whole of stinking hellebore smells fetid and it is, in fact, like the spurge-laurel, poisonous. If you handle stinking hellebore roughly, so as to bruise it, your hands are likely to develop blisters. Spurge-laurel bears oval, fleshy black berries in the summer which, although edible to birds, are poisonous to humans. Both species grow up to a metre (3 ft) high in shallow soils on the chalk in many woods, especially beech woods throughout the North and South Downs, although they are very local and generally uncommon. In both cases their leaves are dark evergreen, though those of the spurge-laurel are leathery, shiny and laurel-like; they are adapted to absorbing the light needed for growth at a time, the winter, before the leaf canopy of the surrounding trees becomes too dense and severely reduces the amount of light reaching the ground.

Turning to more colourful flowers, from March through to May, wood anemones carpet many of the downland broad-leaved woods with their graceful star-shaped white flowers, set off with bright yellow anthers. They nod in the lightest of spring breezes, hence their other name of 'windflower'. At the wood edges and in clearings, and along hedgebanks, they often mingle with the glossy golden-yellow flowers of another member of the buttercup family that blossoms at the same time, the lesser celandine; and sometime also with primroses; and by April with another common plant with yellow-stamened, white, star-like, but slightly smaller flowers, the greater stitchwort, which has a scrambling habit. All of these different plants are pollinated by a variety of early spring-flying insects. With the exception of the wood anemone, which

The stinking hellebore's foul smell is a warning to animals that it is poisonous.

does not produce it, they are a valuable source of nectar for butterflies, bees, hover-flies and bee-flies. In addition bees, beetles and some other insects collect or feed on their pollen.

In April, the wood anemones will also be joined by other woodland plants with white flowers, including masses of the strongly garlic-smelling wild garlic known as ramsons, which has broad green leaves; patches of wood-sorrel with clover-like leaves; and two plants with clusters of small white blossoms, woodruff (bedstraw family) and, by May, sanicle (carrot family). The last named is another species very likely to be found carpeting the ground. Together with ramsons and woodruff it is especially characteristic of calcareous soils, and thus is commonly to be found in the beech and other deciduous woods on the chalk of the North and South Downs. Another characteristic plant of calcareous soil is the rather rare and local herb Paris, a species like dog's mercury, spurge-laurel and stinking hellebore, which has greenish flowers. These consist of four narrow greenish-yellow petals and eight long green stamens with yellow anthers surrounding a berry-like, purple-black ovary with four purple styles, all supported by four lance-shaped green sepals carried on a long stalk above an umbrella-like whorl of usually four large and unstalked, pointed, oval-shaped green leaves with a complex network of veins. It is an altogether unmistakable plant, up to 40 cm (16 in) high, which prefers the damper woods on the chalk.

In the more open downland woods, especially those where oak is dominant, carpets of bluebells will be appearing in flower in April with, here and there, patches of common dog violets and, perhaps not quite so frequently, wood dog violets, distinguished by flowers of a paler violet-blue with straight and un-notched dark violet spurs. Emerging from the woods you are likely to encounter clumps of another species of violet, characteristic of calcareous (chalky or limy) soils, with pale blue-violet flowers. This is hairy violet which is locally common in downland turf almost everywhere on the North and South Downs. It can easily be told from the two dog violets just mentioned by its blunt instead of pointed sepals and the hairiness of its foliage, especially the stalks, which possess long, spreading hairs.

Already certain wild plants have been referred to as characteristic of or even confined to the chalk and limestone. In some species their need to grow on calcareous soils is very exacting: such species include upright brome-grass, tor grass, crested hair-grass, meadow oat-grass, dark mullein, common rock-rose, hairy violet, kidney vetch, dropwort, small scabious, yellow-wort, wayfaring tree and traveller's joy. Of these, traveller's joy is perhaps one of the most useful indicators of calcareous conditions, being a woody plant that climbs over bushes and into trees with an abundance of greenish-white blossoms in summer which are replaced by fluffy greyish-white plumes when in fruit in autumn, giving rise to its popular name of 'old man's beard': it is very conspicuous and the feathery 'beard' lasts right through the winter and into the following spring. It is also very widespread and common on calcareous soils in southern England, including all of the North and South Downs. The caterpillars of certain moths, like the fern, the small waved umber and the rightly named pretty chalk carpet, feed exclusively on traveller's joy and are therefore themselves confined to calcareous areas.

HARES AND RABBITS

Brown hares love the wide spaces of the open downland and are as much at home on the large, cultivated fields as they are on the grasslands. Early spring is *the* time for mad March hares, for this is when the rival males indulge in spectacular bouts of 'boxing', leaping and wild, exciting chases and races; all of which marks the onset of the breeding season (see pages 52–53). Normally, they are solitary mammals, but at this time they congregate in groups, although usually fairly small ones.

Although hares may be born at other times of the year, first litters are generally deposited in spring and there may be as many as four litters annually. There are usually two or three 'leverets' in each litter. They are born fully furred and with their eyes open; and lie low in a depression in the ground, amongst long grass or other vegetation, known as a 'form', and in which they are visited by the doe for suckling. This is their most vulnerable period: if they survive it and reach maturity, then they can expect to live up to four years, although they are actually capable of living up to a dozen years or so. The leverets, which become independent in a month, are prone to attack by buzzards, cats, foxes, stoats and weasels. Intensive farming methods appear to have led to a decline in the numbers of hares in many parts of England, including parts of the North and South Downs. Nevertheless, since they feed from dusk through to dawn and lie low in the daytime, they can be overlooked and populations are difficult to count or estimate. They are usually regarded as an agricultural pest and are often hunted or shot by man, but, although they are known to be fond of turnips and young cereals, their chief natural foods are grasses, clover and sowthistles.

It is questionable whether or not the brown hare is a major agricultural pest, but there is no doubt that, in large numbers, the wild rabbit certainly is. Since myxomatosis decimated the huge British population (estimated at between 60 and 100 million), once this disease became established in 1954, one had only to look at the effect the subsequent absence of rabbits had on the open grassland of the downlands in particular to see what a major factor they were in maintaining short, close-cropped turf, and checking the natural plant succession from grassland through scrub to the woodland climax.

Since the reduction of the rabbit population to near extinction by myxomatosis, the disease has become less virulent and a degree of immunity has developed within the surviving population, so numbers have been gradually increasing. In many areas, including much of the North and South Downs, rabbits are becoming quite common again, and are once more checking the further spread of scrub. However, their numbers vary a good deal from year to year owing to periodic outbreaks of myxomatosis and, to a lesser extent, coccidiosis. The latter can cause a high rate of mortality in young rabbits in dense populations where it spreads easily.

As is well known, wild rabbits live communally in a network of burrows known as buries or warrens. They form social hierarchies in which dominant adult males (bucks) and females (does) maintain their own territories within the warren, and drive away socially inferior (subordinate) animals which do not form territories and therefore mix freely with each other. The subordinates are less successful in breeding. Following a complicated courtship, involving a good deal of chasing of the does by the polygamous bucks, mating takes place. The does then produce their litters of from two to eight blind, deaf and virtually naked young in grassy fur-lined nests at the end of short burrows ('stops'), well away from the main burrow. Most litters are born between January and July at intervals of a month. Ten days after their birth the ears of the young rabbits open, a day later they can open their eyes, and a few days after that they are able to leave the nest and take solid food. They are fully weaned in a month and within four months are sexually mature and capable of breeding.

Although bravely defended by their mother using her powerful hind-legs, many young rabbits, like the adults, fall prey to such predators as buzzards, carrion crows, large gulls, badgers, stoats, cats and dogs, as well as man. Rabbits themselves are almost entirely vegetarian, eating many grasses and a wide variety of agricultural crops and succulent wild plants like dandelions and sowthistles, and the bark of many kinds of young trees. An adult can consume around half a kilogram (1 lb) of fresh green food daily. As it is unusual for them to move more than 200 metres (650 ft) from the warren, the surrounding vegetation is grazed particularly short, thus giving them a good all-round view and reducing the risk of surprise attack. Should this materialize, the alerted rabbit warns the others by thumping the ground with a hind foot and revealing the white underside of its tail (the scut) as it runs to the nearest burrow.

SPRING MIGRANT BIRDS

Among wild birds, many of our winter visitors are only just in the process of leaving as the first of the summer migrants, wheatears and chiffchaffs, begin arriving in March. Bramblings, fieldfares and redwings, for example, may linger until mid-April before setting off for their Scandinavian homelands, by which time willow warblers, blackcaps, nightingales, swallows and others will also have arrived from their African winter quarters. From then onwards the woods and scrub of the downs will be filled with the music of these summer residents as the males establish their territories and advertise their presence in them to the females, which generally arrive a little later: chiffchaffs, willow warblers, wood warblers, blackcaps, garden warblers, grasshopper warblers, whitethroats, lesser whitethroats, redstarts and nightingales. Pied flycatchers and ring ouzels too arrive on the south coast, but do not usually nest in this area, so will continue their journey north and west over the downs to more distant breeding grounds. Most arrive in mid–April and may linger for up to a week in favoured spots before moving on. However, since they are smaller in number and more scattered, they are less easy to detect than on the autumn migration.

The mature, more open beech woods and oak woods are the favoured haunt of the wood warbler, the largest of the resident leaf-warblers. The males shiver their wings as they sing the first and more usual of their two distinct songs from the tree-tops: a short, accelerating grasshopper-like trill lasting up to five seconds. The second song type is a series of plaintive, piping 'pew-pew-pew-pew' notes, uttered once to about every eight repetitions of the trill. Sometimes the male will be seen quite low down, fluttering through and round the trees in a butterfly-like display-flight and singing as he goes.

The grasshopper warbler, or grasshopper-lark as he called it, was a summer visitor which intrigued Gilbert White. Its reeling, bush-cricket-like, rather than grasshopper-like, song can still sometimes be heard at Selborne, on the Common for instance, as well as here and there in scrubby places throughout the North and South Downs. As White himself remarked, the grasshopper warbler's song is ventriloquial in effect and much more like an insect than a bird; he mentioned that 'the country people laugh when you tell them it is the note of a bird.' During the day it usually sings hidden in a thicket; but at dusk and in the early morning it often reels away in full view from a topmost twig with wide-open bill, vibrating with the effort.

The blackcap arrives from Africa in April: its preferred habitats are woodland glades with undergrowth and overgrown hedges.

The male nightingale is, of course, the songster supreme of the woods of south-east England, although in the opinion of some people species like the blackcap run it closely for the honour. It sings, incidentally, as much by day as by night. Sadly, its breeding range has contracted in recent years and its population has declined. This may be chiefly due to recent changes in the

The grasshopper warbler's song is more insect-like than bird-like.

climate of north-west Europe, so there is hope that the situation may eventually be reversed. Fortunately, the nightingale still remains locally plentiful in the woods and copses of most of the North and South Downs up to about 150 metres (500 ft) in altitude. Among places on the South Downs, dense scrub in the valley bottom at Lullington in East Sussex supports many pairs of nightingales as well as grasshopper warblers and other warblers. On the North Downs, localities for both these species include Bookham, Ashtead and Epsom Commons, and the Hog's Back, in Surrey; Selborne in Hampshire; and the Darent Valley and Wye and Crundale Downs in Kent.

A typical species found in scrub with scattered trees on the downland slopes is the tree pipit. In spring the 'parachuting' song-flights of the sweet-voiced males from high perches in the trees attract attention, as also do the insistent and plaintive anxiety calls of both parents when one disturbs them in the vicinity of their nest, which is skilfully concealed amongst the ground vegetation. This species still breeds around Selborne, Hampshire, where Gilbert White knew it well in the eighteenth century, and such other places on the North Downs as Box Hill, Reigate, Dorking, Westerham, Shoreham, and Sevenoaks. On the South Downs the many localities include the Cissbury area, Lullington, Friston Forest and Kingley Vale.

Unlike all the low-nesting species mentioned so far, the redstart nests in holes in old trees, or in nest-boxes, if these are provided. It is found very locally in small numbers in old woodlands on the downlands. Although remarkably well camouflaged in the contrasting light and shade of its woodland habitat, the male redstart is a strikingly beautiful bird, especially when clearly seen on one of its sorties to hunt insects on the ground like a robin. The female, by comparison, has only her quivering chestnut-red tail to relieve her otherwise mainly dull brown plumage. Of the other hole-nesting birds in the old-timbered downland woods, stock doves, jackdaws, nuthatches, great spotted, lesser spotted and green woodpeckers are well distributed and plentiful.

BREEDING BIRDS OF OPEN DOWNLAND

Perhaps the bird that everyone most associates with open downland is the skylark. Its primary breeding habitat is rough grassland, much of which has, of course, been ploughed up on the downlands of southern England since the Second World War; but it has adapted well to the cultivation which has replaced it, nesting on the ground in low-growing crops such as clover, and in the grassy field margins. Unfortunately, the British Trust for Ornithology's ongoing Common Bird Census has revealed a steady decrease nationally of more than 40 per cent in skylark numbers on farmland since 1977. The Trust blames regional specialization of farming, the change from spring to autumn-sowing of cereals, and the impact of modern herbicides for the decline. In spite of this downward population trend, you should experience little difficulty in locating breeding skylarks in open areas of the North and South Downs. Outside the breeding season they will be found wandering the fields in parties or flocks, searching the ground for seeds and invertebrate animals.

The smaller woodlark has been suffering a much more serious decline in numbers since about 1953, which saw the dramatic end of a long period of increase and expansion of its breeding range in England and Wales. However, possibly due to minor climatic changes, this species seems always to have been subject to marked fluctuations in its national breeding population. It is apparently on the upturn again, especially in recently felled forestry plant-ations, where new tree-planting is in its earliest stages. Although few breeding pairs of woodlarks are to be found at present on the downs in Sussex and none in Kent, they are in good strength on the Hampshire–Surrey border area, always a stronghold of theirs. Downland is not their only habitat, heathland being more popular with them, but they are likely to be found wherever there are fairly open areas with low ground vegetation and scattered trees and bushes. Golf courses sometimes provide suitable habitat with their combination of short-mown fairways for feeding and rough areas with scattered trees and bushes for breeding.

Male woodlarks, renowned for their beautiful and plaintive song, sing as much from the high branches of trees as they do in the air, hence the need for trees in the habitat. When song-flighting, they do not usually rise so high as skylarks, but drift round in wide circles as they pour out their lovely melody. Like the skylark, they may be heard singing at most times of the year, except in late summer and the depths of winter. The females construct similar nests to those of the skylark, except that they are not often so well concealed by grass or other surrounding vegetation.

Yellowhammers are widely distributed and plentiful on cultivated and uncultivated downland alike. Its 'little bit of bread and no cheese' song is, of course, one of the most distinctive sounds of hot days in spring and summer in the countryside. The monotonous rattling song of the corn bunting, usually likened to a bunch of keys being jangled, is also unmistakable. Although found on arable land throughout the North and South Downs, it is usually less common and more local than its relative, the yellowhammer. It is yet another seed-eating bird that has decreased on farmland since 1977, by more than 60 per cent, and for probably the same reasons as the skylark. Fortunately, the corn bunting's breeding population has shown a slight increase since 1988. The areas around Cissbury, Lychpole Hill, Jevington, Lullington and Beachy Head are among places on the South Downs where corn buntings as well as yellowhammers will be encountered, while on the North Downs localities for both include the Darent Valley and the adjacent downs, and in several places along the dip slope between Dartford, Longfield and Faversham.

SPRING BUTTERFLIES

As spring advances, the early butterflies, brimstones, small tortoiseshells and the like, which have emerged from the places where they hibernated through the winter as adults, will be joined by the first of those which spent the winter in the pupal (chrysalis) state: grizzled skippers, large, small and green-veined whites, orange tips, holly blues and speckled woods. All of these will appear on the wing before the end of April in a warm, sunny spring, by which time there will be nectar-bearing wild flowers in great plenty to satisfy their energy demands. Speckled wood butterflies, however, are exceptional in that they rarely imbibe from flowers, preferring to suck up honeydew (the sticky excretions of aphids) from the leaves of trees.

Typically, the speckled wood is an inhabitant of shady woodland rides and borders as well as shady lanes with well-developed hedgerows. In such situations it is common almost everywhere on the North and South Downs. The males occupy sunny spots in their habitat, perching on leaves from which they sail out to investigate passing individuals of their own species. An encounter with a female may lead to courtship and mating, but when the

intruder is a male a skirmish develops in which they fly up and down, revolving around each other, until either the defending male returns victorious to his perch in the sunny spot, or the other wrests it from him. The defending male usually seems to win and hold on to his territory in such encounters. Incidentally, its pattern of cream-yellow spots on a dark-brown background camouflages the speckled wood well amongst the sunlight-dappled leaves of its rather dark woodland home. In spring, when the leaf canopy of the woodland trees is more open, these creamy spots are larger than on the butterflies of the summer generation when relatively few shafts of sunlight penetrate the canopy. As a further protection against surprise attack from birds, this butterfly is furnished with a false eye-spot on the top of each forewing and three eye-spots on the rear of each hindwing, which draw an attack away from the vital head and body. Normally the speckled wood is on the wing in two main generations from April to September.

Although, like the speckled wood, not restricted to calcareous ground, the diminutive grizzled skipper butterfly is nevertheless one of the characteristic butterflies of the chalk downs, especially on sunny, yet sheltered slopes, and in clearings and broad woodland rides where there are plenty of flowers. It flies very fast, so it is only when it has settled that you can see its distinctive black and white chequer-board pattern, and the long, grizzly-grey body scales which are

The cuckoo normally arrives around the middle of April. A female usually parasitizes the nests of only one other species.

47

responsible for its vernacular name. The first grizzled skippers appear on the wing as early as the third week of April in a forward year, although May and June are the best months to look for its usually small colonies where the larval foodplants, wild strawberry, cinquefoils, silverweed and agrimony, are plentiful. It has become scarcer at the eastern end of the North and South Downs, but is still locally common elsewhere in spite of the loss of much of its habitat to the plough and the spread of dense scrub.

The spring butterfly *par excellence* is undoubtedly the graceful orange tip. Flying along the flowery waysides and woodland rides and borders, the males, with their conspicuous splashes of orange colour on their white forewings, are the very epitome of high spring. The females lack the orange colour and are therefore easily overlooked among the many and rather similar green-veined whites and small whites flying at the same time; they lay their greenish eggs,

Barlavington Down. Early June.   John Davis

which soon turn orange, singly on the flower-heads of various cruciferous plants (members of the family Cruciferae, with four-petalled flowers arranged crosswise) of the wayside, especially garlic mustard (Jack-by-the-hedge) and lady's smock.

The open chalk grassland and scrub at Barlavington Down provide cover for partridges and ample food plants for spring butterflies.

LIZARDS AND SNAKES

By the middle of April common lizards will be much in evidence and, as far as the more observant naturalists are concerned, adders and grass snakes too. Both lizards and snakes emerge from the holes and crevices where they have hibernated through the winter early in March and, being cold-blooded, spend as much time as they can basking in whatever sunshine there is, as long as

49

temperatures rise above 10°C. This is a good time to see them as they tend to be sluggish so early in the spring; but one must, of course, be careful not to tread on an adder. Later, when it is warmer, these poisonous snakes are much more alert and then normally move off rapidly at the approach of human beings. Naturally, it makes sense to wear suitable footwear when wandering in areas likely to harbour them: not flimsy sandals or bare feet. Adders are only likely to bite if surprised; even so, the poison is rarely fatal in the case of healthy adults. Nevertheless, hospital treatment should be sought as quickly as possible.

The adder or viper, as it is also called, is to be found in the more open parts of the North and South Downs, as long as the turf and ground cover is not too short. Sometimes it occurs in open woodland, although the grass snake is more likely to be seen here. Sunny, south-facing slopes and banks, or on tree stumps and fallen trees, are the types of places where it may be discovered basking. When the sun becomes too hot there is less chance of seeing snakes, although the grass snake is more tolerant of heat than the adder and may be found basking until the temperature rises above 20°C before it too will seek the shade. Lizards are even more tolerant of the sun, with the exception of that legless lizard, the slow worm, which tends to avoid it, and does not bask as nearly as much as the others. The slow worm, incidentally, is common throughout the North and South Downs where there is sufficient cover; but in spite of this it is not often seen, except by those who know how and where to search for it, because it is secretive and tends to conceal itself. It is most easily found by lifting and looking under logs and other pieces of wood, flat stones and discarded sheets of metal. Slow worms are, of course, perfectly harmless, incurring our favour by eating many slugs and other invertebrates which are considered to be injurious to our horticultural interests.

Common lizards, too, are absolutely harmless and feed entirely upon invertebrates, such as insects and spiders. Like the slow worm, if attacked themselves and seized, as often happens, by the tail, they can detach themselves from it and escape. Subsequently, a new but imperfect tail grows in its place. It is therefore easy to identify those that have escaped in this way. Usually, their great agility and speed in darting back into cover enables lizards to avoid natural predators like falcons and other birds, rats and weasels.

During April common lizards mate. There is little or no courtship, the male merely chasing the female and seizing her in his jaws before copulating. In contrast, adders and grass snakes both have a more sophisticated courtship in which the male crawls actively alongside the female and constantly licks her with his tongue. The walker on the downs at this time of year may be lucky enough to come upon the so-called 'dance of the adders' in which two males wrestle for the right to mate with a nearby female. They sway and rear up at each other, and move rapidly over the ground as they grapple vigorously.

Both adders and grass snakes catch and eat small mammals, small birds and their eggs and young, lizards, frogs and toads, although the adder is not so fond of the amphibians as the grass snake, which is more likely to be found in damp places and by the waterside where toads and especially frogs are to be found.

Grass snakes swim well and readily enter water in pursuit of such prey; on these occasions they may also take fish, newts and tadpoles. Because of its affinity with damper habitats, the non-venomous grass snake, although widespread throughout both the North and South Downs, is more likely to be seen in the river valleys that cut through them, like the Arun, Adur, Ouse, Cuckmere, Wey, Mole, Darent, Medway and Great Stour.

HOBBIES, KESTRELS AND SPARROW HAWKS

Lizards and small snakes are often taken by kestrels and that other small falcon, the hobby. Kestrels, especially, swoop on and catch common lizards. However, their chief victims are field mice, voles and other small mammals, plus small birds (particularly house sparrows in urban areas), worms, beetles, grasshoppers and other insects. Hobbies do not hover in the distinctive manner of kestrels, but catch their prey on the wing, using their superior speed and manoeuvrability to great effect, catching even fast flyers like swifts and swallows, as well as large dragonflies and other large, flying insects. Sparrow hawks use a different technique altogether: they fly fast and low through woods and along and through hedgerows and shrub, and take small birds (on which they prey almost exclusively) by surprise, snatching them up in their sharp talons. As well as birds up to the size of a pigeon, they sometimes capture small mammals and insects, often pouncing on them from a perch. Occasionally, sparrow hawks may fly above the trees, especially in the spring when the pairs soar above their intended breeding sites on short, broad-tipped wings which contrast with the long, sharp-pointed ones of kestrels and hobbies.

Kestrels and sparrow hawks are widely distributed and plentiful as breeding species throughout the downlands of our area. Although, because of its more secretive behaviour, the sparrow hawk is less often encountered, in well-wooded parts of the downs its population density may, in fact, be greater than that of the apparently more numerous kestrel. Both species have recovered well from the marked decline in their populations in the 1960s caused by eating birds contaminated with organo-chlorine pesticides, which were subsequently banned. The hobby, always a very local species, has recovered too; most pairs of this summer resident are to be found on the more westerly downs, especially in the Hampshire–Surrey border area and in West Sussex, with fewer in East Sussex and fewest on the North Downs in Kent.

WILDLIFE OF THE SEA-CLIFFS

An exciting feature of the North and the South Downs is the way in which they have been cut through by the circulation of the sea through what became the English Channel after the Last Ice Age, separating them from their counterparts in France, and leaving precipitous and spectacular white chalk cliffs. Those at

BROWN HARES

The most interesting and visually exciting time to watch brown hares is in spring. March is, of course, the month of the proverbial 'mad March hares'. They were thought to be mad at this time because of their bizarre bouts of 'boxing', wild chasing and leaping. In fact, all these amusing activities are concerned with the courtship of the does or Jills (females) by the bucks or Jacks (males), and the rivalry between the bucks for the does. Curiously, despite its conspicuousness in bare fields on the downs and elsewhere, the courtship behaviour of hares still remains to be fully researched.

Although most often to be seen in March and April, courting can be observed in February and May, while I have watched it as late as 5 June. So preoccupied do the hares become in their sexual excitement that they take heed of little else, and may not notice the quiet approach of a human observer. I was once nearly knocked off my bicycle by two large bucks in headlong pursuit of a doe which suddenly appeared from behind a hedge and raced across a farm road just in front of me. I was later able to watch the doe feeding in sugar beet while the two bucks sat up on their haunches and sparred with their forelegs like boxers (exactly as portrayed by John Davis in one of the pictures in the plate), and then vigorously chased each other in and out of an adjacent uncut hayfield. When sparring, hares often stand upright on their hind legs. They may not always be rival bucks; sometimes it can be a doe repulsing the unwanted attentions of a suitor (top left).

The four hares playing 'follow my leader' in the top centre right picture are three bucks hopefully pursuing a doe, while the two animals at the extreme top right are a couple of rival bucks: the one on the right appears to be appeasing the aggression of the other buck by submissive behaviour involving the grooming of its hind foot. When not absorbed in courtship activity, hares are acutely sensitive to potential dangers and have long, efficient sound-collecting ears and large eyes, as the head study shows, plus a highly developed sense of smell. When danger threatens, they crouch close to the ground with flattened ears to avoid detection, often looking, even at a short distance, like a brown clod of earth. If they are discovered or stumbled upon, they leap to their feet with a great jump and bound off at high speed on their long legs. As they demonstrate in their rivalry chases, they can manoeuvre, when pursued, with great dexterity and skill, changing direction sharply, doubling back, and even performing somersaults. Owing to their exceptionally long hind legs, they are least good at running downhill, preferring to descend diagonally or, better still, run uphill. They know their extensive home territory extremely well and cling to it tenaciously.

Dover (North Downs) are, of course, famous, but perhaps the cliffs of Beachy Head (South Downs), rising to 163 metres (535 feet) are even more impressive. The rise of sea-level following the Ice Age cut Kent and Sussex off from the rest of the European continent before many animals and plants, incapable of flight, had managed to spread far enough north-west following the retreat of the ice and the improvement in the climate, to recolonize land vacated with the onset of the glaciations. Thus, many species are to be found in plenty on the French downs which are absent here. A comparison of the fauna and flora of the chalk downs on either side of the Channel makes a fascinating field of study.

In south-east England, the tops of these sea-cliffs, as well as holding plants and animals typical of those farther inland, have a selection of species all their own. Looking first of all at the bird-life, the sheer cliff faces do not afford many ledges suitable for nesting sea-birds like the guillemot. Nevertheless, small numbers of guillemots used to nest on the cliffs of Kent and Sussex, but eventually died out by 1930. However, the fulmar petrel, which was not known to breed in the past, began prospecting the cliffs around Folkstone and Ramsgate in the 1960s and now nests in small numbers here and there (for example, between Newhaven and Peacehaven, and at Cuckmere Haven) all along the sea-cliffs of the North and South Downs. This rather gull-like sea-bird that possesses even greater mastery of the air, has undergone a huge population explosion and expansion of breeding range in the past two hundred years. It did not arrive in Shetland, in the north of the British Isles, from Iceland and the Faeroes until 1878. By 1922, however, the species had penetrated south down the east coast of Scotland and begun to prospect for breeding sites on the first of the English sea-cliffs. This remarkable increase of range has been linked with the climatic amelioration during the last half of the nineteenth century and the first half of this.

Fulmars attract attention to their nest sites on the cliff ledges by their noisy, cackling mutual displays. The pairs take it in turn to sit on their single, large white egg which is laid in a bare scrape anytime from mid-May to early July. Another recent colonist, the kittiwake, has also been increasing on the Kent and Sussex cliffs. Herring gulls and, occasionally, lesser black-backed gulls also nest wherever there are suitable cliff ledges, and on roof-tops in the coastal towns of Dover, Folkestone and elsewhere. Here and there other, sheltered cliff ledges may be used by the occasional pair of kestrels or, with increasing frequency recently, peregrine falcons.

Like the sparrow hawk and hobby falcon, the peregrine falcon suffered severely from pesticide poisoning in the late 1950s and 1960s, with the result that the British breeding population was almost decimated. Since the persistent organo-chlorine pesticides ban was introduced, it has made a steady recovery and in recent years has gradually re-established itself in many of its former haunts. Now it is attempting to breed again on some of the cliffs of Kent and Sussex. Peregrines are fierce and relentless hunters which strike fear in the many species of birds, some as large as curlews or mallard, upon which they prey. They take many feral pigeons and jackdaws which, along with the herring gulls and kittiwakes, are their commonest cliff-dwelling neighbours.

The feral pigeons and jackdaws do not actually breed on ledges, but in crevices in the cliff-face. A bird which actually builds its nest on the cliff-face is the house martin, whose cup-shaped nest made of mud is so familiar under the eaves of houses. In fact, cliff-faces are the natural home of house martins where they may nest in large colonies similar to those under bridges. Usually the nests are fixed in cracks and crevices, and may not always be easy to see. One such sea-cliff colony is to be seen at Folkestone Warren.

A much less common bird of the sea-cliffs is the dark-coloured rock pipit. The males draw attention to their presence in the spring by their song-flight, characteristic of pipits, in which they rise to a height of 5 metres (16 ft), then parachute down with expanded wings, singing as they do so, to land on the cliff top. The rock pipit's song is not so melodious and protracted as that of the tree pipit, but stronger than that of the otherwise similar meadow pipit's, which also nests in small numbers along the cliff-tops of the Kent and Sussex Downs, such as those at Cuckmere Haven and Peacehaven, Sussex.

As one would expect there are plants and insects, in addition to birds, which are special to the sea-cliffs and are not usually found inland. These include such plants as the wild sea cabbage, sea beet, rock samphire, yellow horned-poppy, seaside or slender thistle and dwarf centaury; and moths such as the marbled coronet and the white spot. From May to August, the pale yellow flowers and large, greyish-green leaves of wild sea cabbage are as conspicuous a feature of the dazzling white cliffs at Dover as they were in the days of the 'Father of English Botany', William Turner (1508–68), who recorded them there before 1548. Curiously, while abundant on the chalk cliffs around Dover and Folkestone, the plant is now considered extinct on those in Sussex. Although the ancestor of the cultivated cabbages, which are so vulnerable to insect attack, Dr D. F. Owen has pointed out that the wild cabbage is remarkably resistant to the depredations of insects, apparently because the latter have not been able to overcome its chemical defences. The flowers, however, of the wild sea cabbage are as readily visited by nectar-seeking insects, like bees, butterflies and flies, as are their garden relatives when allowed to blossom.

During his visits to Dover, William Turner also noted, among other species, two more plants with yellow flowers growing in plenty on the Dover cliffs – rock samphire and yellow horned-poppy. Rock samphire, which belongs to the carrot family (Umbelliferae), has long been prized for the sake of its fleshy leaves which taste good when pickled. Although it does not flower until June, continuing through to September, its deeply divided, fleshy green leaves are easily recognized on the cliffs here and there in Kent and Sussex.

Typically, yellow horned-poppy is a seaside plant of the shingle beaches, as at Cuckmere Haven; it also grows on non-calcareous rocks, but in the area of the North and South Downs is sometimes common along the chalk cliffs. The large flowers, up to 9 cm ($3\frac{1}{2}$ in) across, are deep yellow and appear from June till September. They are succeeded by long, up to 30 cm (12 in), sickle-shaped seed-pods. As with most other seashore plants, its grey-green leaves are rather fleshy and have a waxy bloom.

Among the moths which visit the cliff-top flowers at night are two noctuids which are largely confined to calcareous districts: these are the marbled coronet and the white spot. Both are attractive species with dark brown forewings strikingly patterned with white; the former with a truly marble-like effect and the latter with most of the white concentrated into a conspicuous spot or blotch. The white spot is much the rarer of the two, being confined to a scattering of localities along the coastal chalk cliffs (for example, between Newhaven and Eastbourne) and shingle beaches (for example, Dungeness) of Kent and Sussex, where its caterpillars feed only on Nottingham catchfly, a sticky plant of the sea-cliffs found only locally. The catchfly's pinkish or whitish flowers open at night to give off their scent. This not only attracts the adult moths of the white spot, but various other night-flying moths as well, including the marbled coronet. When they are on the wing from the end of May to July, both the marbled coronet and the white spot also visit the flowers of the

catchfly's relatives: the sea campion, red campion and white campion, as well as viper's bugloss and red valerian. The caterpillars of the marbled coronet feed on the ripening seeds of various species of catchflies and campion, particularly sea campion and bladder campion.

The resident rock pipit nests in rocky crevices in downland coastal cliffs: the fulmar also nests locally on these cliffs.

MILKWORTS

During May and June the downland turf is often brightened by the blue flowers of milkworts. Two of these are widespread and locally common on both the North and South Downs: chalk milkwort and common milkwort. The prettiest of the two is the former, which has small blossoms of a particularly bright, clear blue, but sometimes also of a paler blue, pink or white. The flowers of the common milkwort are also variable: although usually a deep blue,

57

mauve, magenta, pink or white ones are frequently to be seen. The chalk milkwort can be told from the common milkwort by its irregular rosette of broad leaves at the base of its stem, which the other lacks. A very lucky and sharp-eyed botanizer working the North Downs in the West Kent and Wye districts might come across a third species of milkwort, the Kentish milkwort, the smallest and least bright of them all. Because of its few and insignificant slate-mauve flowers it is very inconspicuous and easily overlooked.

LATE SPRING BUTTERFLIES AND MOTHS

By May more species of butterflies will have joined those, like the small tortoiseshell, speckled wood, green-veined white, orange tip and brimstone, which began to appear already in early spring. These include such species as the dingy skipper, green hairstreak, small copper, common blue, small blue, brown argus, adonis blue and small heath. None of these, with the exception of the adonis blue, are found exclusively on calcareous downland, but, nevertheless, flourish particularly well on it.

The green hairstreak favours sunny, sheltered glades and paths amongst scrub, as long as it is not too dense, and woodland borders. However, it is quite likely to be found frequenting more open downland, provided it is sheltered and its chief larval foodplants, bird's-foot trefoil and common rock-rose, are plentiful. Green hairstreaks fly in May and June; only the females seem to visit flowers regularly, which may be of various kinds, including dandelions and hawkweeds. The males are territorial and occupy perches on prominent plants from which they make sorties to investigate any passing butterfly or insect of comparable size, in the hope that it is an unmated female. The green hairstreak is the sole British butterfly with genuinely green wings: only the underside though – the uppersides of its wings are brown. Although it is still locally common, it is somewhat less so than it was half a century ago; but plenty of colonies remain along the North and South Downs, especially the farther west one travels.

Apart from the green hairstreak, the other species listed above are characteristic of open grassland, especially where wild flowers grow in profusion. Some of these wild flowers, notably the bird's-foot trefoil, horseshoe vetch, kidney vetch and common rock-rose, are the larval foodplants of certain butterflies and day-flying moths. For instance, the caterpillars of the dingy skipper, green hairstreak and common blue butterflies, the chalk carpet and straw belle moths, and three species of burnet moths all feed on bird's-foot trefoil. The dingy skipper is a drab, rather moth-like butterfly which flies rapidly on sunny days in May and June, darting from flower to flower. When roosting at night, or during overcast daytime conditions, it rests in a Noctuid moth-like attitude on the dead flower-heads of knapweeds and other plants. Quite often dingy skipper caterpillars are found feeding on horseshoe vetch as well as bird's-foot trefoil on the chalk downs. The species is locally common throughout the North and South Downs and may also be seen flying in some lowland sites, such as the flowery meadows of the river valleys which cut through the downs.

The commonest and most widespread British blue butterfly, the common blue appears on the wing in May and June as a first generation and as a second from late July to the end of September. Apart from bird's-foot trefoil, its caterpillars feed on various other leguminous plants, including restharrow and white clover. When fully grown, the caterpillars are often 'milked' by ants for a honeydew-like secretion of amino acids from an abdominal gland. It seems likely that, in return, the ants afford the caterpillars protection from the attacks of predacious insects. This association with ants is more highly developed in other blue butterflies, such as the adonis and chalk-hill blues. Mention must also be made of another member of the blue butterfly family (Lycaenidae); this is the brown argus, which is a little smaller than the common blue and has the same flight periods, except that the summer flight is over by mid-September. It is unusual in that both sexes have chocolate-brown coloured wings bordered with orange-red blotches, whereas only the females of the common blue and the other species are brown, the males being some shade of blue without orange marginal blotches or spots. The caterpillars of the brown argus feed chiefly upon the leaves of common rock-rose, hemlock stork's-bill or crane's bills, and the species is generally locally plentiful wherever these plants occur on the North and South Downs.

The smallest of the blue butterflies in Britain, the small blue, is a characteristic insect of chalk and limestone hills, although it also occurs on coastal sand dunes. It forms discrete colonies, often very small, in warm, sheltered places which receive much sun and where its larval foodplant, kidney vetch, grows in some profusion. The small blue females, which are sooty brown like the males, but lack their powdering of blue scales, deposit their light blue-green eggs singly among the youngest kidney vetch flower-buds. When they hatch, the caterpillars bore into the flowers to devour the ovary and developing seeds. As they grow towards maturity, the pale brownish-yellow, pink-marked caterpillars feed with their heads in the flowers and their tail ends sticking out. When full-grown, about early August, they descend to the ground and search for hibernation sites, under moss or in soil crevices, where they remain until the following spring. On emerging they no longer feed, but climb the stems of mosses or grasses and pupate there, attached by a silken girdle and pad. Some may subsequently be carried away by ants and buried in underground earthen cells from which the perfect butterflies apparently emerge safely between mid-May and mid-July. In August a partial second generation occurs in most years in southern England.

Small blues do not fly much, spending most of their time basking or feeding at flowers. Like the brown argus, they have lost many of their former haunts to agricultural development or to the luxuriant growth of scrub and other coarse vegetation due to the dearth of rabbits following myxomatosis. However, they are still locally numerous on both the North Downs and the South Downs.

Nature reserves where they occur include Castle Hill National Nature Reserve, East Sussex, and Old Winchester Hill National Nature Reserve, Hampshire.

One other butterfly whose first generation appears on the wing in May and June and which should be mentioned, at least briefly, is the small heath. An orange-brown little butterfly with eyespots on the tips of its forewings, it is usually common on grasslands with scattered scrub everywhere in the British Isles, including calcareous grassland. It is, in fact, one of the typical butterflies of the North and South Downs. Small heaths do not visit flowers as freely as some other butterflies, and will usually be seen flying lazily just above the grass tops, but are capable of flying fast when the need arises. The males hold territories, flying out from their perches to intercept passing butterflies of other species as well as females of their own kind. Small heath caterpillars feed on grasses with

fine leaf blades such as fescues and annual meadow grass. There is a second generation of adults in July and August and sometimes a third in September.

While walking over the downs during May and June you are almost sure to come across such attractive day-flying moths as the burnet companion, Mother Shipton, latticed heath, small purple-barred and common crimson and gold. The last two are diminutive, yet colourful moths which fly actively in the sunshine, visiting, among others, the flowers of their larval foodplants, common milkwort and wild thyme respectively. The small purple-barred is characterized by the purple-red cross band on each of its olive-brown forewings, while the common crimson and gold's forewings are purple with yellow blotches and spots, and its hindwings are black, banded with purple and yellow, plus a yellow spot and a streak. There is another recently separated and

Adonis blue butterflies, seen here with swallows on Mill Hill near Shoreham-by-Sea, Sussex, are restricted to calcareous soils in southern England.

Mill Hill 28 June
Gotman

very similar species, except that it is duller with paler yellow spots, whose biology and distribution in Britain is yet to be defined; but it apparently occurs on the downs in south-east England. A second generation of this species and of the common crimson and gold fly in July and August. At first sight, a burnet companion moth feeding at a flower can be mistaken for a dingy skipper butterfly until its unclubbed antennae and partly orange-yellow hindwings are seen clearly. It derives its popular name from its tendency to fly in the same places and visit the same flowers as the gaudy-coloured burnet moths. Its relative, the strikingly patterned, brown and cream-coloured Mother Shipton, receives its name from the supposed resemblance of the markings on its forewings to the profile of a well-known medieval witch. It flies readily in the sunshine or when disturbed, but soon lands again following a short, swift flight. The remaining moth mentioned, the latticed heath, is one of the large family of Geometer moths and also flies when the sun shines in May and June, and again, as a second generation, from July to September. Latticed heaths are often abundant where they occur, one or two flying up with almost every step you take. This is usually where the larval foodplants, lucerne, clovers and trefoils, on which the caterpillars of the burnet companion and Mother Shipton also feed, grow in great quantity. The black chequer markings on a cream or white background make the latticed heath an easy moth to recognize.

BOX HILL AND TREES TYPICAL
OF CHALK DOWNS

Most, if not all, of these late spring-flying butterflies and moths can be seen on Box Hill on the North Downs, near Dorking in Surrey. Rising to nearly 200 metres (650 feet), it is one of the most famous landmarks south of London and, along with other sections of the steep downland escarpment, survives relatively unspoiled under the management and protection of the National Trust.

Box Hill acquired its name from the conspicuous and dense growth of box trees on the precipitous cliff-like slope which rises nearly a hundred metres (300 feet) above the River Mole. Few other plants are able to grow under the dark shade of the closed canopy of small, oval, leathery and shiny evergreen leaves of this renowned box wood, one of the very few such woods in Britain. In fact, the box is only known as a native British tree in a few other places on the North Downs (for example, Boxley Hill, Kent), the South Downs, and the Chiltern and Cotswold Hills, although it has been introduced in many localities elsewhere in the country. Box is best known as a bushy shrub, but left undisturbed in the wild it can become a small, rather round tree up to 11 metres (36 feet) high. Its greenish blossoms bloom from March to May, clustered in the axils of the leaves, and are pollinated by flies. Black seeds are released by brown seed capsules in September.

On Box Hill, the well-developed box trees are probably a final stage in the ultimate or climax vegetation of chalk downland, although beech is the usual climax tree, with yew and juniper as secondary elements. Yew is another round-shaped evergreen tree, but in fact a conifer, which also shades out plants endeavouring to grow beneath, especially when many grow together to form a wood as at Box Hill, and at Buckland Hill and Ranmore nearby, and, best of all, at Kingley Vale National Nature Reserve, near Chichester in West Sussex. This last-named wood is huge and is thought to be the finest natural yew forest in Europe. Some of the largest trees in it are reputed to be up to 500 years old.

The foliage of yew is dark green and rather sombre. It contrasts in autumn with the bright red, fleshy berries, each of which envelops a single large seed. Although much eaten by birds, which void the seed unharmed in their excreta, both seeds and fruit are highly poisonous to man and other mammals. So is the foliage, which is sometimes eaten by cattle with dire results. Birds seem to have an enzyme in their digestive tract that neutralizes the toxic alkaloid taxine present in yew. The male flowers bloom on separate trees from the female flowers. Both are greenish, but the male blossoms are brightened by numerous yellow stamens; the female ones are egg-shaped. They appear in March and April and are pollinated by the wind.

Another evergreen conifer, characteristic of the southern chalk, although it also grows on heathland and moorland in the north, is the elegant, yet wind-resistant juniper. It therefore grows happily on the exposed escarpment of Box Hill and here and there elsewhere on the North and South Downs, either as a shrub with spreading branches or as a narrow, conical-shaped tree up to 6 metres (20 ft) in height. The blue-green, spine-tipped leaf needles are arranged in whorls of three and have a fragrant smell of resin about them. In May and June the juniper's small flowers appear at the base of the leaves and, like those of the yew, the male ones, which are yellow, usually appear on different trees to the female, which are green. Following pollination by the wind, the female flowers are succeeded by green berry-like cones which gradually turn bluish-black through different shades of blue before ripening in their second or third year. Among other uses they are used for flavouring gin.

The most characteristic tree of the chalk downs is undoubtedly the handsome and stately beech. As already mentioned, if chalk vegetation is not interfered with by man and other animals, beech woodland forms the natural ultimate vegetational climax. Such woods are a common feature of the southern downlands, especially on the North Downs. Where they have developed along the escarpments they often form so-called 'hanging woods' or 'hangers' like the Hanging Wood on the North Downs Way, south-east of Caterham, which can be seen from the M25 motorway near Junction 6. Much better known is Hampshire's Selborne Hanger, the beech wood on the escarpment overlooking Gilbert White's home 'The Wakes'.

Beech trees can grow to a lofty height of over 36 metres (120 feet), developing massive grey trunks and branches, and roots which spread out from the trunk above and just below the ground. They are thus well adapted to growing on shallow, fertile soils of the kind found on the chalk downs. The flowers appear in April and May at the same time as the new, shiny

yellow-green leaves: the tassels of greenish-yellow male flowers on long stalks and the unstalked greenish-white female ones are found on the same tree, the latter being pollinated by the wind.

Among other trees and shrubs which typically grow on the downs are common or purging buckthorn, dogwood, field maple, spindle, wayfaring tree, whitebeam and wild privet. The presence of all of them, more or less growing together, is a clear indication that the soil is very calcareous. The wayfaring tree, which rarely grows above 6 metres (20 feet), displays its conspicuous, dense umbrella-like head of creamy white flowers over a short period lasting from the end of April to mid-May. It was given its original English name of wayfarer's tree by the sixteenth-century botanist and herbalist John Gerard because it was such a familiar tree to him along the old roads and tracks. Later the name became corrupted to wayfaring tree. Like the purging buckthorn, dogwood and wild privet, it produces black berries in late summer and autumn, although they are red at first. The berries of all four species are bitter and quite inedible to human beings, but are eaten by birds. So are those of

spindle and whitebeam, which are red not black, though over-ripe whitebeam berries used to be made into a jelly and eaten with venison.

Spindle berries are four-lobed and a distinctive pinkish-red in colour, quite different from the shiny scarlet of whitebeam. Together with field maple, whitebeam and purging buckthorn, it flowers in May and June, while dogwood and wild privet produce their blossom in June and July. Those of the last two, dogwood and whitebeam, are white, whereas field maple and purging buckthorn have yellow-green or greenish flowers. Dogwood flowers are visited by flies and other insects, including the rose chafer, a large beetle, which eats its pollen. Although pollinated by the wind, the insignificant flowers of field maple, a characteristic ingredient of hedgerows on the downs, are also visited by flies, and sawflies. The profuse white blossoms of wild privet are popular with many insects, particularly butterflies such as the hairstreaks, meadow brown, brimstone, peacock, red admiral, and white admiral. The foliage of all these downland trees and shrubs provides homes and food for the larvae of a wide variety of insects.

The wayfaring tree is typical of chalk scrubland, as here at Box Hill. The magpie is a highly adaptable bird that is commonly seen both in urban areas and the countryside.

65

S U M M E R

S omewhere around the middle of June, in the average year, summer
takes over from spring. The days become more reliably warmer,
even hot, as high summer arrives in July and stretches into August.
The fresh green flush of new foliage and great masses of blossom on
the hawthorns and other trees, so characteristic of spring, are
gradually replaced by darker, deeper hues of green. As the canopies of the beech
and oak woods close, so they become shadier and perhaps more sombre. By late
summer the vegetation looks rather tired and dusty, and, if the summer has
been a hot and dry one, the downland turf may well become parched, and
yellow rather than green. Indeed, on the open, exposed grassland many of the
more susceptible wild flowers will become dried up in such droughts. As a
result, those butterflies and moths whose caterpillars feed on them will suffer
accordingly and may well become scarcer than usual. Grasshoppers, which like
hot conditions, may, on the other hand, flourish as they are able to survive well
on parched grass.

Bird song, with a few exceptions, becomes less evident as summer
progresses, as most male birds are paired and busy helping their mates to rear
their voracious young; therefore they no longer need to sing to advertise their
presence to a prospective mate. Moreover, relatively few unmated males will
be around to challenge mated males for their females or territories; so territorial
behaviour, the other main reason for song, tends to break down, and with it the
output of song generally. In those songbirds which rear more than one brood in
a season there may be a brief revival of territory re-establishment and singing.
One of the exceptions to the general rule, referred to a moment ago, is the
yellowhammer. The male's wheezy ditty is one of the most characteristic
sounds of the 'hazy, lazy days of summer' on the downs. This is because,
although first brood egg clutches may be found as early as May, the peak of the
yellowhammer's breeding season is in summer.

In the downland woods many species of birds become more elusive and
difficult to see because they are feeding themselves and their young hidden in
the dense foliage, often high up in the canopy. Furthermore, the separation of
the different species by sound alone is complicated by the similarity to each
other of some of their calls and the begging cries of their fledglings. And, of

A barn owl hunting at dusk. Its soft feathers enable it to fly quietly and to take its prey — small mammals — by surprise.

67

course, some of these fledglings, lacking the distinguishing plumage features of their parents, can only be identified when the latter are seen feeding them. Away from the woodlands, identification is easier and infinitely more comfortable than looking up at the canopy. On the other hand, craning one's neck upwards to look at a rock pipit, black redstart or some other bird perched high above on such sheer cliffs as those at Dover can be equally uncomfortable.

BIRD-LIFE OF THE DOWNLAND COAST TOWNS

The black redstart has actually nested recently on the massive Shakespeare Cliff, the entry point for the Channel Tunnel, a little to the west-south-west of Dover; but since its colonization of south-east England, which began in the 1920s, it has more often nested in the town of Dover itself. The main influx of breeding black redstarts into England occurred during the Second World War when several pairs began nesting in the ruins of bombed buildings, not only in Dover, but in central London and other towns and cities too. With the clearance of the bombed sites and their replacement with new buildings, the black redstart, whose truly natural habitats are the rocks and cliffs of the mountainous regions of central and southern Europe, has tended to switch to tall, complex industrial buildings like power stations. These offer a good selection of holes and sheltered ledges as nest sites. Still a rare breeding bird in England, more often seen on passage at migration times, the black redstart began expanding its range north-westwards in Europe about 1870, apparently in response to the climatic amelioration which commenced about that time. A few pairs continue to nest in Dover and other neighbouring coastal towns. Across the English Channel they are plentiful in the ports and towns along the Continental coast.

To a bird like the black redstart, nesting on buildings is not so very different from doing so on the cliffs and broken rocks of its original, natural habitat. This is true of a number of other cliff and rock-nesting species that also find human buildings, with their many ledges and crevices, an effective substitute for the real thing. It is not really surprising therefore that such birds as herring gulls, lesser black-backed gulls, kittiwakes, kestrels and feral pigeons (descended from rock doves) are to be found nesting on buildings, especially in coastal towns.

The British breeding populations of herring and lesser black-backed gulls have grown enormously in the course of the present century; presumably in response, at least partly, to the greatly increased sources of food available in the form of refuse and sewage associated, in turn, with the even greater expansion of the human population. Since the 1940s, the resulting shortage of natural nesting sites, especially in areas within close range of the richest feeding places, led many of these large gulls to make the simple transition from cliffs to roof-tops. So far, however, practically only herring gulls have done so in the seaside towns of the area that comprises the North and South Downs. Their nests are often situated on flat roofs or placed up against a chimney-stack or parapet.

*The spotted flycatcher
in its typical erect pose,
watching for passing
insects.*

That true 'seagull', the kittiwake, has also begun nesting on seaside buildings on the east coast of England since the 1950s, including Dover.

Kestrels often nest on buildings, especially tall ones such as churches and towers, not only along the coast but inland as well. Sometimes they nest on high window-ledges and can be observed from within by the fascinated human occupants of such buildings. Feral pigeons, starlings, house martins and house sparrows have, of course, long been adapted to nesting on our houses and in our gardens, and are as numerous in the seaside towns of Hampshire, Kent and Sussex as they are everywhere else.

DOVER: GATEWAY TO ENGLAND FOR BIRD AND INSECT COLONISTS

Because of its position at the end of the shortest sea-crossing from the European mainland, Dover has always been the chief gateway into England for human travellers. It is also the shortest route for insect travellers and has often been the point of entry, not only for regular migrants and irregular wanderers, but also for those attempting a colonization of Britain. For example, although that attractive little Noctuid moth, the varied coronet, previously occurred as a rare vagrant in south-east England, it was not until 1948 that it was discovered to be invading Kent through Dover, following a previous extension of range in north-west Europe. In that year a local amateur entomologist captured eleven of the moths visiting sweet-william flowers in his garden in the town. The caterpillars of the varied coronet feed on the ripening seeds of this popular garden plant (sometimes those of bladder campion as well), and during the late summer of 1949 he collected a number of sweet-william flower-heads and reared several more moths from the caterpillars living in them. It was then discovered that most sweet-william plants in Dover contained varied coronet caterpillars. By the following year, the moth and its caterpillars were abundant around the town and had begun to fan out from this bridgehead into the surrounding districts. Since then the varied coronet has colonized much of our area, becoming a common garden insect, and is continuing its spread through southern England as far west as Gloucestershire and as far north as Lincolnshire.

This species is but one among some 26 species of moths which have colonized Britain from the Continent since 1850, mostly through Kent and Sussex, and have become either permanently or temporarily established. All these invasions have followed marked expansions of range north-westwards through western Europe, presumably prompted by the general amelioration of the climate since the middle of the nineteenth century. The same cause appears to have been responsible for the parallel spread of other insects and many species of birds.

Curiously, one of the most characteristic birds of the downland villages nowadays is another invader and colonist which was unknown in Britain before 1952 – the collared dove. The first breeding pairs invaded from the Low Countries by way of Norfolk, where they nested in 1955. In the early 1970s the

The glow worm – in fact a carnivorous beetle – attracts a mate with its bluish-green light.

ROMAN SNAIL AND GLOW WORM

70

total British population was estimated to be in excess of 100,000. All this followed on from an incredibly rapid spread north-westwards across Europe, once they had crossed the River Danube early in the 1930s from the Balkans, which were colonized soon after 1900 from Turkey.

WILD FLOWERS OF THE ARABLE FIELDS

Outside the villages, the crops grown on the cultivated downlands include such fodder crops as clovers, lucerne and sainfoin. All these are members of the Leguminosae, the pea family, and, like other legumes, fix nitrogen in the soil through the action of bacteria within their root nodules. Clovers and lucerne, and especially sainfoin, bear attractive blossoms during the summer which are highly attractive to many insects, particularly bees and butterflies. The bright pink-red lupin-like flower spikes of sainfoin are quite lovely, so it is a pity that, like lucerne, it is less popular a crop than formerly. Fortunately, it is a chalk-loving plant, and like the others, it grows commonly as a weed at the edges of other crops or on the uncultivated downland turf throughout the North and South Downs. Fields of lucerne (also called alfalfa) and clovers are among the best places to look out for the clouded yellow and the much rarer pale clouded yellow butterfly during a good summer for these immigrants from continental Europe. Strong immigrations of both species are scarcer than they used to be, but the North and South Downs are among the best areas in southern England to see them. The females of both clouded and pale clouded yellows lay their eggs on the leaves of lucerne, clovers, sainfoin and other leguminous plants.

Not surprisingly, many of the weeds of arable land on the downs, like shepherd's purse, field bindweed, fumitory and that artist's delight, the common corn or field poppy, are by no means restricted to them and are common in cultivated fields elsewhere. However, there are some wild plants which are particularly addicted to calcareous soil and, though characteristic of the downland turf or places where the soil is thin and the chalk exposed, have become common weeds where the downland slopes have been ploughed up, and crops, especially corn, planted. One of these is wild parsnip, which belongs to the carrot family (Umbelliferae), and from June to September is easily recognized by its loose, flat umbels of small, yellow blossoms. These are highly attractive to many insects such as hover-flies, soldier beetles, ichneumon-wasps and social wasps. Incidentally, it is advisable to avoid handling the coarse hairy foliage and stems of the plant on sunny days as this may cause blisters, especially to sensitive skins. When damaged wild parsnip emits a strong, pungent smell. Often the plant will be found growing in masses around the edges of fields, beside paths, and in rough grassy places.

The very poisonous deadly nightshade or belladonna, as it is also called, is a typical plant of chalk and limestone, and rare away from it. It is locally plentiful throughout the North and South Downs in shady spots in and around the edges of woods, and amongst scrub, and in hedgerows bordering cultivated land.

Although not a weed of cultivation, it is convenient to discuss it here with its evil-smelling close relative, henbane, which is also widespread on these downs, but uncommon. Like henbane, all parts of the plant are poisonous, but it is the large, cherry-like fruits, which are shiny black when ripe, that sometimes tempt people, especially children, to eat them, with dangerous or even deadly results. Henbane fruits are much less inviting. In spite of its toxicity to human beings, many other animals are able to eat the foliage of deadly nightshade without ill-effects, including rabbits and various insect larvae; while some species of birds readily eat the berries. The dull, purple-brown, drooping, bell-shaped flowers, some 2.5–3 cm (about an inch) in length, are borne in ones or twos at the bases of the rather large, pointed oval leaves from June to September. Both species are somewhat stout and bushy in appearance, and may grow more than a metre

(3 ft) high. The purple-veined and centred, dull yellowish flowers of henbane open from June to September.

In contrast, field mouse-ear, another typical species of calcareous soils, is a low, creeping plant that often forms mats on the ground in bare places around the edges of arable land, as well as in dry, sparse grassland. In such places it is locally plentiful on both the North and the South Downs. From other mouse-ears on the downs, it is easily recognized by its large white flowers, up to an inch (2.5 cm) in diameter, which look like those of the greater stitchwort, and flower from April until August. As its English name suggests, ground-pine, also a low-growing and even prostrate plant, resembles a diminutive, grey-green bushy and hairy pine tree, and smells of pine resin when bruised. It actually belongs to the mint family, and from May to September produces bright yellow flowers

Juvenile wheatears near the Long Man of Wilmington in late summer.

5th September
Wilmington   John Davis

characteristic of the Labiates, with tiny red dots on the lower lip. Ground-pine is a very local and uncommon plant that only grows where the soil is very chalky. It needs open ground and therefore does well, where it occurs, as a weed of cultivation. It is found in a number of places on the North Downs in Kent and Surrey, but seems to be almost extinct on the South Downs.

SOME BIRDS OF ARABLE DOWNLAND

The arable fields of the downs are home to a variety of birds which have adapted themselves to the annual rotations of crops and farming operations. Some species have accomplished this more successfully than others. The least successful are those species, like the grey and red-legged partridges, and the stone curlew, that have found it increasingly difficult to cope with the growing mechanization and intensification of farming practices since 1940, and especially since 1960, allied with the widespread use of modern herbicides and pesticides. Some crops are harvested earlier than formerly was the case, thus causing heavier losses to nesting birds. The enlargement of fields, through the widespread destruction of hedgerows and other field edge cover, has not helped either. It has resulted in the loss of many relatively safe nesting sites. The use of toxic chemicals, moreover, has caused serious declines in the numbers and diversity of agricultural weeds and insects available as food for birds. The speed with which stubble is ploughed in these days has also been an adverse factor.

One of the early and worst-affected casualties of modern agricultural techniques has been the stone curlew, once a familiar and typical bird of open expanses of downland in Sussex and elsewhere. Gilbert White knew it well and wrote in 1768 that it 'abounds in all the campaign parts of Hampshire and Sussex'. He mentioned that they congregated in vast flocks in the autumn near the house of a Sussex friend who farmed near Chichester. He himself heard and saw stone curlews regularly on the downs around his Hampshire home at Selborne, making 'a clamour which may be heard a mile', and shot them 'before the pointers in turnip-fields'.

At the beginning of the nineteenth century, stone curlews continued to be quite common on the South Downs, according to W. H. Hudson, writing in 1899, 'and bred on all the barren stony spots on the highest hills, as well as on the extensive shingly flats on the Pevensey coast'. Although they suffered from much egg-collecting by shepherds – no doubt to earn a few extra pounds from egg-collectors and dealers, as they did selling trapped wheatears to poulterers, their numbers did not seriously decline until the 1870s. By the 1890s only a very few pairs still attempted to nest in such downland areas as the neighbourhood of Chanctonbury Ring, between Steyning and Storrington, and by Jevington, near Eastbourne, with varying degrees of success or lack of it.

With the relaxation of such persecution following the introduction of improved bird protection acts, and the depressed state of agriculture in the two decades after the First World War, the stone curlews of the South Downs recovered from near extinction. In Sussex, numbers built up to around 60 pairs before 1940. However, with the advent of the Second World War, agriculture once more became very important and formerly cultivated downland was brought back into production and additional pristine downland turf ploughed up. Thereafter, the Sussex population declined to about 20–25 pairs by 1973. Today only a pair or two attempt to nest on the more remote and barren parts of the South Downs, or in arable fields not subject to the most modern farming methods. The stone curlew, a summer resident from Africa, is on the north-western edge of its breeding range in England, so there is the distinct possibility that the wetter, more maritime climate of north-west Europe since about 1870 has also played a significant part in its decline. Wet springs and summers have a bad effect on the activity and, therefore, availability of the stone curlew's principal prey of lizards, bush-crickets, grasshoppers and other large insects. The invasion of what was open downland by scrub since the myxomatosis epidemic decimated the rabbit population in the late 1950s also rendered unsuitable some former stone curlew haunts.

A streaked, sandy-brown coloured bird, the stone curlew looks superficially like a large plover with large, staring yellow eyes, lapwing-shaped bill and long, yellowish legs with thick knees, hence its country name of 'thick-knee'. When it flies, usually low over the ground, with trailing legs and rather slow wingbeats, and long glides, it reveals an unmistakable black and white wing-pattern with two conspicuous white bars. On the ground it stands in a characteristically hunched attitude and runs with its head held low in a furtive manner. When danger threatens, stone curlews often rely on their effective camouflage, crouching low and flattening themselves to avoid detection. They are most active at dusk and after dark, and it is at this time that their loud and wild, wailing curlew-like calls are heard. All of them have migrated south by early November, but return early in spring, during March or early April.

Intensive agriculture, if it continues to increase, could send the once common native grey partridge the same way as the stone curlew – downwards to extinction or near extinction. The introduction and widespread use of herbicides and pesticides in the 1950s led to a dramatic decline in the numbers of grey partridges. Research revealed that the eradication of the insect food of partridge chicks, directly by insecticides and indirectly through the destruction of their natural foodplants, was causing high chick mortality. Moreover, as agriculture grew more intensive from the 1960s, the desire for larger fields in which to work farm machinery more efficiently led to the removal of many hedgerows, and the consequent loss of nesting habitat and reservoirs of insect food. Fortunately, in spite of their general decline since the 1950s, grey partridges are still widely distributed throughout the North and South Downs.

Another partridge, the red-legged, is also widely distributed over the North and the South Downs. Currently, it is doing rather better than the grey, owing to the frequent release of captive-bred stock by field sportsmen, who seem to prefer it. Many of these commercial introductions now consist of hybrids between the red-legged or French partridge, as it is also called, and the similar

chukar partridge of Asia Minor. To make matters more complicated, pure chukars and the very similar rock partridge of south-east Europe are also being released for shooting purposes. Red-legs feed upon much the same food as grey partridges – mainly plants, including grain, and some insects; the latter are also especially important in the red-leg chick's diet.

A small relative of the partridges, the quail, a summer visitor to Britain, has also suffered from changes in farming practices, such as the mowing of grass earlier in the season than used to be the case; heavy shooting in southern Europe where it winters; and the change between about 1850 and 1950 to a generally wetter, more maritime climate in north-west Europe. Formerly a common breeding bird, its numbers declined drastically during that period, apart from the occasional exceptionally good year for immigration, and it became a rarity. Since 1942 an upward trend in the quail population has taken place in continental Europe, and the years of high immigration into Britain have tended to become more frequent, presumably due to the present trend towards a drier climate with more frequent hotter summers.

During these good quail years, the North and South Downs have received their fair share of calling birds, easily recognized, even when not seen, by their persistent and characteristic 'wet-my-lips' call, heard in hay meadows and cornfields. Proof of breeding is much more difficult to obtain, but many were suspected of having done so: possibly 30–35 pairs in 1987, for example.

Britain is just outside the natural range of the little owl, but the speed with which it became established over England and Wales, following its artificial introduction in the late nineteenth century, showed that conditions suit it here. It probably failed to advance quickly enough north-westwards after the Last Ice Age to colonize Britain before the rising sea-level cut off the last land links with the continental mainland. Its population, apart from minor fluctuations, now seems pretty stable. Breeding pairs are to be found nowadays scattered throughout the North and South Downs, but they tend to be under-recorded by bird-watchers. Although they may occasionally be heard calling in the daytime or flushed from a resting place in an old tree, little owls are crepuscular birds and therefore most active in the evening; at this time they hunt for mice and voles, small birds going to roost, earthworms, large moths and beetles, and other invertebrates. Their barking, yelping and mournful 'kiew' and 'poor' calls are quite easily recognized, once learned.

The turtle dove, closely related to the collared dove, is one of the most characteristic birds of the downland woods and thick scrub in summer. Its soft, rhythmic and continuous purr has a soporific effect and is the very epitome of lazy summer days when the downs are bathed in hot sunshine. You can hear it in many places along the North and South Downs and may often disturb turtle doves from a roadside or wayside track, or from drinking at a puddle or pool, when they fly off with distinctive flicking movements of their wings. At the same time they reveal their rufous backs and black tails, edged with white, so different from those of the collared dove, which are khaki-brown above and black and white under the tail. Turtle doves feed on the seeds and foliage of such wild plants as fumitory, and will be seen visiting the arable fields where this and other plants grow as weeds. In late summer, towards the end of the breeding season, they often collect in parties or flocks, some of them quite large; they may then be seen perching in rows on telephone wires over or beside the fields, especially corn stubble. In August and September these flocks leave the downs for the south coast, and migrate through western France and Spain to their winter quarters in West Africa.

Throughout the summer, stock doves and wood pigeons feed in the same downland fields as the turtle doves, and by late summer they, too, are gathering in flocks. Some of the wood pigeon flocks are already quite large at this time and contain many juveniles. They are joined by large flocks of other birds, containing high proportions of juveniles, such as rooks and jackdaws, starlings, house sparrows, greenfinches and linnets. At the same time seeding thistles and other weeds will also be attracting colourful, musically tinkling 'charms' of goldfinches, as well as parties of linnets.

HEDGEROW BIRD-LIFE

Hedgerows make highly favourable nesting places for finches such as the linnet, chaffinch, greenfinch and goldfinch, as well as yellowhammers, dunnocks (hedge sparrows), magpies, whitethroats, lesser whitethroats, blackbirds, song thrushes and wrens. One of the most typical of hedgerow birds on the downs is the whitethroat, a summer visitor which arrives in Britain in April from West Africa. In spring the rather scratchy and discordant, but cheerful, song of the male attracts attention, particularly when he flies rapidly up above the hedge in an excited song-flight, then dives down again as if exhausted. Often the singer flits ahead of you for a hundred metres or so before doubling back or just vanishing into the tangled foliage. A good view of him will reveal his conspicuous white throat, which contrasts with his grey head and pinkish breast. When excited, he often raises the feathers of his crown.

The turtle dove is smaller than the other common doves of the region. Unlike the resident collared dove, it returns to Africa in the autumn.

The whitethroat's cousin, the lesser whitethroat, is by no means a lesser bird, although a few millimetres shorter; but it is more secretive and usually more local and less common. The male's typical song is very different from the whitethroat's, being a loud, monotonous rattling sound rather similar to the rare cirl bunting, and a little like the yellowhammer's without the 'cheese' bit at the end. The singer, hidden in the depths of the hedgerow, is usually difficult to see. When one approaches closer, a quiet, softer whitethroat-like warble is often heard preceding the characteristic rattle song. When the lesser white-throat does show itself, it will be seen that it is greyer than the whitethroat (both sexes look much alike) without the whitethroat's rufous back, but with a blackish patch behind the eye, giving it a masked look. Its white outer tail feathers are also less obvious.

Breeding lesser whitethroats are usually well distributed in small numbers throughout the North and South Downs where suitable tall hedgerows, festooned with brambles, honeysuckle and traveller's joy, occur. By August they begin to leave their breeding sites and prepare for their migration to wintering grounds in the semi-desert regions of north-east Africa congregating along the south-east coasts at such places as Beachy Head in East Sussex, and the North and South Forelands in Kent. By October few are still to be seen.

Another typical hedgerow bird of the downs is the linnet, a common breeding finch throughout the North and South Downs in spite of a marked decrease of more than 50 per cent on farmland during the period 1977–88. Fortunately, the British Trust for Ornithology's Common Bird Census reported a recovery of 27 per cent on farmland in 1989, thus bringing the breeding population back to its level five years previously. As a primary consumer of weed seeds as well as insects, the linnet is particularly vulnerable to modern intensive agriculture, so it is reassuring to learn of this recovery.

The sustained twittering song of the male linnet is musical and attractive. At the end of the breeding season adults and juveniles assemble in flocks, frequenting oilseed rape and other seed-bearing crops, or searching stubble fields and marginal land of the downlands in search of weed seeds. By autumn these flocks may number several hundred birds, although 50 to 200 is more usual.

HEDGEROW PLANT AND INSECT LIFE

The most obvious feature of well-established downland hedgerows is the richness of their plant and insect life. Even in summer, when the glorious blaze of spring blossom on their major constituent trees and shrubs, like blackthorn, hawthorn, wayfaring tree and whitebeam, has faded, they will be succeeded by the creamy-white of dogwood and wild privet, and the glorious pinky-white flowers of dog rose and sweet-briar. Beneath, the hedge bottoms and adjacent verges will be bright with a varied assortment of herbaceous flowers – the white umbels of hogweed and wild carrot, crowded with a colourful variety of flower beetles, bees, wasps, saw-flies, hover-flies and other insects; the showy deep blue flowers of meadow crane's bill and tufted vetch; white and red campions; the pinks and reds of mallows; the maroon of hedge woundwort; and rich golden-yellow masses of St John's worts and yellow toadflax. All these and others will be busy with butterflies and other nectar-seeking insects.

In most places the commonest of the butterflies flitting along the hedges, basking in the sunshine and sucking nectar from bramble blossoms and other flowers, will be the meadow brown and its aptly-named relative, the hedge brown. The latter is also often called, almost as aptly, the gatekeeper, because of its habit of seemingly loafing around field gates. The meadow brown appears on the wing between mid-June and October on southern downland, whereas the hedge brown begins to fly about a month later and continues into early

79

September in an average year. They hedge brown will sometimes be seen flying on the downs well away from hedgerows and woodland borders as long as there is some scattered scrub; the meadow brown will often be seen doing the same as it is a typical grassland butterfly, and is usually found in great numbers on the chalk of the North and South Downs. Although the ringlet is a characteristic butterfly of damp and sheltered places, as befits its dark sombre appearance of chocolate-brown with yellow-ringed, false eye-spots on its underwings, it is surprisingly common on the rather dry downland, provided there is sufficient shade along wood edges and hedgerows, and amongst scrub. The caterpillars of all three species feed on grasses.

The various trees and shrubs contained in the hedgerows and woodlands of the downs support the larvae of a large and varied insect fauna. Among them one can pick out for special mention some of those butterfly and moth species which feed on trees and shrubs especially typical of the chalk downs, such as beech, field maple, dogwood, purging buckthorn, spindle and wild privet. Purging buckthorn, together with its relative alder buckthorn, which is much more characteristic of low-lying, damp ground than the drier soils of the chalk, where it is rare, is the foodplant of the velvety-green, finely black-speckled, caterpillars of the brimstone butterfly. These handsome caterpillars can be found resting in the daytime, well camouflaged along the midribs of the leaves,

Hedgerows and woods on the downs provide habitats for a wide variety of birds, mammals and insects, such as these stag beetles.

from May until they pupate in July underneath the buckthorn leaves or twigs, or those of neighbouring plants, to which they attach themselves horizontally by a silken pad and girdle. The pupae, from which the butterflies emerge in about two weeks, closely resemble a leaf. Purging buckthorn is also the foodplant in late spring of the usually green caterpillars of the dark umber moth, which flies on the southern downlands in July.

The buckthorns belong to the dogwood family of plants, and dogwood itself is a host to the caterpillars of the holly blue and green hairstreak butterflies, and of the yellow-barred brindle and triple-spotted clay moths, although none of these late-spring or summer insects are confined to the downs. Holly blue caterpillars may sometimes also be found feeding on the flowers and fruits of spindle as well as dogwood and, more usually, holly and ivy. Spindle is the only known foodplant of the larvae of the attractive scorched carpet moth, whose mainly white wings do actually look as if they have been scorched. This moth is double-brooded on the southern downs and flies in May and June, and again in August, more or less wherever spindle grows. Its caterpillars, therefore, should be looked for on that shrub in June and July, and again in September.

Wild privet nourishes the caterpillars of several species of moths, including the coronet, lilac beauty, orange moth, privet hawk, scalloped oak, swallow-tailed moth, waved umber, and willow beauty, as well as being an alternative foodplant for the yellow-barred brindle. Of these, the privet hawk, with a wingspan of between 10 and 12 cm (4 to 5 in) one of our largest moths, is the most impressive. Its huge and fat, bright green caterpillars, with their seven purple-edged, white oblique body-stripes and fearsome black tail horns, used to be found more easily on the trim garden privet hedges of suburbia but it is not as common now. It is still relatively plentiful in most parts of the North and South Downs, however, even if not as numerous as formerly. The splendid moths fly like small aeroplanes at dusk, in June and July, probing a wide range of deep-tubed flowers in gardens as well as on the downs, especially honeysuckle. The caterpillars, therefore, will be found in July, and become fully grown in August: the adult butterfly will emerge the following summer.

The caterpillars of Lepidoptera to be found feeding on blackthorn and hawthorn on the downs, as elsewhere, are too numerous to list but they include the brown hairstreak butterfly (only on blackthorn), and moths like the lackey, oak eggar, lappet, emperor, magpie, brimstone, early thorn, swallow-tailed and light emerald. Of these, the caterpillars of the emperor, the lappet and the oak eggar grow to a large size before pupating. That of the emperor is the most colourful, being green with black-bristled yellow warts on black bands or hoops, once it has grown out of its early stage of being black with a yellow lateral stripe. In both stages it is well camouflaged amongst the foliage of the blackthorn or hawthorn (and other foodplants such as bramble or heather) on which it feeds from late May to August. It may attain a length of 6 cm (2½ in) before constructing a stout, fibrous brown cocoon in which the blackish-brown pupa overwinters until April or May when the moth emerges. Both sexes are striking in appearance with big false eye-spots. The female flies only at

BADGERS

These sketches made in September and October by John Davis show some of the typical activities that the human badger-watcher will see during a crepuscular vigil at this time. It is an important season for badgers as they must take full advantage of the abundance of food in autumn to build up their fat reserves and ensure their survival through the hardships of winter. High summer may well have been a difficult time for them, especially if it was very dry, as food is sometimes hard to find then and involves a relentless search for it through the twilight and night. If they, particularly the young ones, survive this tough period, then life becomes easier for them and they can expect to find sufficient food to put on enough fat for the winter.

They eat all kinds of things, being true omnivores. Earthworms, however, are their staple diet, and this explains why it is difficult for them to find enough food when the ground is bone-hard through summer drought or winter frost. In droughts they will switch to some other relatively easily obtainable food, like cereals or various insects, especially bumble bee and wasp larvae, and, in cowpats, dung beetles and their larvae. In addition they will kill and eat various small mammals and their young up to the size of hedgehogs and rabbits; also birds and their eggs and young, amphibians, snails and slugs, and, in times of shortage, carrion. Wasp nests are often dug up in late summer or September when the colonies are at their biggest, the thick fur of the badgers being seemingly impervious to the stings of the frenzied wasps. At this time of year, the autumn fruits – blackberries, rowan and yew berries, acorns, beechmast, hazelnuts, chestnuts, windfallen apples, pears and plums, and edible fungi – become readily available.

As John Davis's notes indicate, the badgers emerge soon after sunset to stretch, scratch, play and sniff the air before setting off along their well-worn paths on their nocturnal feeding forays. On emerging from the sett, they need to scratch vigorously like the one in the illustration, to relieve themselves of the irritation caused by their particular species of lice and fleas, and perhaps in an attempt to get rid of them. The fleas breed in the bedding material (dry bracken, grass, leaves, moss, etc.) with which the badgers line their underground bedchambers, so it is not surprising that they bring out old bedding at intervals, like the one is doing at the bottom of the page, and dispose of it outside the sett. It is replaced with fresh bedding collected and brought in bundles on suitably dry nights, autumn being one of the peak periods for this activity.

Badgers can be very noisy between emerging from the sett and commencing to forage, particularly during the peak mating season from February to May, when they bark, growl, purr, 'whicker' and even scream, and later when the cubs play vigorously.

11th September
Cool night. 1st emerged 7·50pm
sunset 7·25pm

September 18th
1st (Boar) emerged
7·15
sunset 7·05

22nd October
6·30 pm

Bringing out bedding

John Davis '91

night, but the smaller, more colourful male flies rapidly over the downs when the sun shines. He is attracted to virgin females by their powerful scent. The emperor moth is plentiful in many parts of the North and South Downs.

Male oak eggar moths, too, fly fast on sunny days over the downs in a zig-zagging manner, seeking the stationary unmated females, who fly only at night, and attract them by emitting powerful scent pheromones; but both sexes fly later than the emperor – in high summer (July and August). Like the emperor moth, the female oak eggar is larger and thicker-bodied than the male, and not so brightly coloured in brown and yellowish hues as him. Oak eggar caterpillars hatch in August or September, but may be found most easily in April or May when they emerge from hibernation to feed not only on blackthorn and hawthorn, but bramble, sallow, oak and various other trees and shrubs. Like the lappet, lackey and other members of the Lasiocampid family of moths they are very hairy and should therefore he handled with caution as the hairs easily break off and may cause an unpleasant skin rash. The brown hairs of the oak eggar caterpillar grow thickly from its dark body, which shows as rings between the soft pile. Down each side of its body there is a line of white marks. When full grown in June or early July they measure as much as 6.5 cm ($2\frac{1}{2}$ in). The oak eggar is quite common over most of the North and South Downs.

Field maple, an attractive hedgerow tree with neat yellow-green leaves, is home to the larvae of several moths, including the maple prominent, plumed prominent, maple pug, the mocha, barred sallow and the satellite. The two prominent moths, the maple and plumed, belong to a family of fast, night-flying moths, which are readily attracted to artificial light. The family name of 'prominent' refers to the tuft of scales protruding from the middle of the hind margin of each forewing that stands erect when the moth has settled on a resting place. Both species, brown in colour, are largely restricted to areas where field maple grows on the calcareous soils of southern England. The maple prominent is the commoner of the two, especially along the North Downs, on the chalk of east Hampshire and the South Downs in West Sussex. Elsewhere on the South Downs, they are both very rare or absent. In fact, the plumed prominent, whose name comes from the plume-like antennae of the male, is found only here and there on the North Downs, and on the east Hampshire downs, where it flies late in the year – in November and December. The maple prominent flies from May till July, its wrinkled whitish and greenish-blue caterpillar feeding on field maple leaves from July to September, while the largely blue-green caterpillar of the plumed prominent does so from late April to early June.

WILD ORCHIDS

The chalk downs of southern England are the best places in Britain to look for wild orchids. The North Downs and South Downs are especially rich in the variety of species found there, and are the British strongholds for such species as the violet helleborine, musk orchid, early spider orchid, lady orchid, monkey orchid, burnt orchid and man orchid. The late spider orchid is found only as a very rare plant of chalk grassland, occurring in a few scattered colonies in a restricted area of the North Downs in east Kent. It looks very like the bee orchid, but can be separated by the two upper petals, which are small and usually green in the bee orchid and larger, broader, triangular and pink in the late spider. The bee orchid, although much reduced by the ploughing-up of downland turf and reduced grazing by rabbits and sheep in the past fifty years or so, is still locally plentiful throughout the North and South Downs, and may be seen flowering in June and July on some of the nature reserves open to the public. As its name implies, the early spider orchid flowers much earlier than the late spider orchid – in April and May – and is easily recognized by its yellow-green sepals and petals, and the distinctive glossy blue, double-pronged mark on its furry, bumble bee or fat spider-like lip. Although not as rare as the late spider orchid, it has also suffered from the intensive cultivation and reduced grazing of the past fifty years, and is now very local, being confined to the Kent and East Sussex downs, and the Isle of Purbeck in south-east Dorset. Most of these localities are near the sea, and the orchid is quite plentiful in some of them, such as the Beachy Head area of East Sussex, and between Dover and Folkestone in Kent.

These three orchids of the genus *Ophrys* have all evolved bee-like flowers which invite male solitary (non-social) bees to copulate with them; not only through their visual resemblance to a female bee of the right species, but also by emitting a scent similar to that produced by her. As a result of this remarkable and highly specific relationship cross-fertilization is effected. The male bee, in attempting to mate with the conspicuous bee-like lip of the orchid flower, comes into contact with the club-shaped pollinia, a pair of pollen balls attached by slender stalks to sticky pads contained within the bursicle, a membranous pouch on the single anther. Directly the bee touches the bursicle it bursts and releases the sticky pads of the pollinia, which become attached to it so that the bee flies off to another orchid with the pollinia sticking upright from its head. As the bee flies on, the pollinia swing forward so that they are perfectly adjusted to make contact with, and fertilize, the sticky stigma of the next receptive orchid flower of the right species visited by the bee.

In France and Sweden studies of the late spider orchid have shown that its flowers are pollinated in this way by large male solitary bees of the genus *Eucera*. As regards the bee orchid, such studies as have been made in England of this much commoner plant suggest that it is normally self-pollinated: a couple of days after the flower opens, the pollinia fall from the anther on to the sticky stigma below. Nevertheless, more observations are needed of the possible part solitary bees and perhaps other insects play, since they are known to visit bee orchids quite regularly around the Mediterranean.

Another *Ophrys* orchid, the fly orchid, is known to be regularly pollinated on the Continent by two species of solitary wasps, *Gorytes mystaceus* and *G. campestris*, attempting to copulate with its fly-like flowers; but they have apparently not yet been seen visiting them in Britain. This should not be too difficult to prove as the fly orchid is widely distributed in England and Wales, and locally quite common on both the North and the South Downs, flowering in May and June. It is, however, a slender, unobtrusive orchid and is quite difficult to detect amongst the grass growing in its favoured habitat of scrub and woodland edge. Its flowers, too, are small and dark, each with a long and narrow chocolate-brown lip, which has a metallic-looking blue patch in the middle. The two upper petals are dark and thin, and look rather like the antennae of an insect, thus making the whole flower very like the dark-coloured females of the pollinating wasp species.

The North Downs in Kent not only contain the only British colonies of the late spider orchid, but are the chief stronghold of the lady orchid. Moreover, Kent shares with Oxfordshire and Yorkshire the few remaining monkey orchids left in England. Outside Kent the lady orchid is only known as a great rarity in Surrey and Sussex, but over much of the Kent downs it is widespread and locally common, being found in small colonies. It is a tall and magnificent orchid, with a long and dense flower-spike of fragrant pink or white flowers studded with minute tufts of crimson hairs, and hooded with deep purple-brown flecked green sepals. Each individual flower is reminiscent of a Victorian lady in a spotted crinoline dress wearing a dark purple bonnet, hence the plant's apt English name. Lady orchids will be found flowering in May and June in sheltered, but rather open woods, wood borders and scrub where the soil is chalky.

Apart from these Kent specialities, the county is renowned as the best in England for wild orchids, not only rare species, but also for the relative abundance of some of the commoner ones. Man orchids are generally more common and widespread in Kent than elsewhere, although they are also well represented in Hampshire and Surrey. So called because of the supposed resemblance of its individual flowers to little yellow men, sometimes edged with red or chocolate colour, wearing a flat hat or helmet, the man orchid normally blooms in June. It can grow to a height of up to 40 cm (16 in) and should be sought for on the grassy downland slopes, amongst light scrub and along the edges of woods.

The downland woods, especially the beech woods, are the habitat of a number of interesting orchids; among them the broad-leaved or common helleborine, white helleborine, violet helleborine, narrow-lipped helleborine, green-flowered helleborine, common twayblade, bird's-nest orchid, greater butterfly orchid, lesser butterfly orchid and the spring-flowering early purple orchid. Of these, the narrow-lipped and green-flowered helleborines are very local and must therefore be counted as rare. Perhaps the most fascinating common orchid of the beech woods is the bird's-nest orchid, a curious yellow-brown, leafless plant that lives saprophytically on decaying accumulations of dead leaves. It is plentiful in many of the beech woods of the North and South Downs, including Selborne Hanger in Hampshire, where Gilbert White already observed it in the eighteenth century, and around Box Hill, Surrey. Greater and lesser butterfly orchids are not confined to beech woods, both also growing in other woods and amongst scrub on the open downland slopes, and flowering from May into July. These elegant orchids with sweet-scented (especially strong at night), creamy-white flowers tinged with green, are pollinated by night-flying moths, the pollinia becoming attached as they feed, to their probosces (tongues) in the case of the lesser butterfly and to their heads with the greater butterfly.

The more open grasslands of the North and South Downs carry a rich and varied assortment of wild orchids, especially in the more unspoilt areas, such as around the Darent Valley, Wye and Crundale Downs in Kent, Box Hill in Surrey, around Ditchling Beacon in Sussex and on the chalk hills around Winchester in Hampshire. The common or relatively common species are autumn lady's tresses, fragrant (sweet-scented) orchid, bee orchid, fly orchid, burnt orchid, green-winged (green-veined) orchid, common spotted orchid and pyramidal orchid. Here and there, the very local and rare species which may occur are musk orchid, frog orchid, early spider orchid, late spider orchid, lady orchid and man orchid. Some of these have already been discussed; of the remainder, the fragrant or sweet-scented orchid and the pyramidal orchid are very characteristic of the chalk, and are widespread and generally common almost everywhere on the North and South Downs.

Like the two species of butterfly orchid, both the fragrant and pyramidal orchids specialize in attracting Lepidoptera (butterflies and moths) to pollinate their strongly scented pink blossoms. The scent of the pyramidal is not so pleasing to our sense of smell, being rather sweetly fox-like, but that of the fragrant certainly is. The individual flowers of all four species have long, slender spurs containing nectar, a characteristic of orchids pollinated by Lepidoptera. When a visiting butterfly inserts its proboscis (tongue) into a flower and spur of either a fragrant or a pyramidal orchid, a pair of pollinia placed at the entrance to the spur become attached to it by their sticky pads (a single, saddle-shaped one in the case of the pyramidal orchid). As with other orchids, when the insect leaves the flower, the pollinia quickly swing forward at right angles, ready to make contact with the stigma of the next flower.

The pollination of all these orchids was studied by the great Charles Darwin around his home, Down House, in the village of Downe, on the North Downs in Kent, close to the London borough of Bromley, and the results published in 1862 in his book *The Various Contrivances by which Orchids are Fertilised*. In particular, he studied them at his beloved and now famous 'orchid bank', on the side of a valley near to Downe village. The delightful grassy slope, amid woods of beech and yew, still looks much the same as it must have done in Darwin's time. Fortunately, it is lovingly protected and cared for by the Kent Trust for Nature Conservation, from whom permission must be sought to visit it (*see* Useful addresses on page 183). Most of the orchids observed by Darwin still continue to grow there, including twayblade, fragrant, pyramidal and common spotted. Apart from its wild orchids, the bank's other typical chalk flora includes hairy violet, marjoram, salad burnet, silverweed, squinancywort, viper's bugloss, white mullein and yellow-wort.

Just as Charles Darwin's long residence at Downe, Kent, has made the otherwise obscure little North Downs village famous throughout the world, so, in the previous century, had that quiet, studious curate Gilbert White made the equally small Hampshire village of Selborne at the western extremity of the North Downs where they join the South Downs, even more famous through his classic book *The Natural History of Selborne*.

Selborne village lies below a fine example of a downland hanging wood, Selborne Hanger. This consists almost entirely of beech: in White's words '... the most lovely of all forest trees, whether we consider its smooth rind or bark, its glossy foliage, or graceful pendulous boughs'. The Hanger has changed little since he wrote about it in 1767, and still contains most of the typical plants of beech woods on the chalk that he mentioned, including autumn gentian, bird's-nest orchid, broad-leaved helleborine, spurge laurel and stinking hellebore. It still resounds in spring to the calls and songs of many of the birds that he, as a keen ornithologist, studied, like the chiffchaff, willow warbler, wood warbler, nightingale, nuthatch and green woodpecker. The house martins, swallows and swifts, whose breeding biology he described so elegantly, are still breeding in good strength in and around the downland village of Selborne.

Wildlife of the Downland Rivers, Streams and Ponds

The streams which emerge from the springs below the water table of the chalk hills are notably clear, and many plants and animals thrive in them. They contain such characteristic fish of chalk streams as the bullhead (or miller's thumb), lampern, trout, eel and plenty of three-spined sticklebacks.

Whereas chalk streams like the Oakhanger at Selborne arise from spring-lines at the base of the chalk and flow outwards into the Weald from below the escarpments, or from the north-facing dip-slopes of the North Downs to join the River Thames and from the south-facing dip-slopes of the South Downs into the sea, the main rivers that cut their way through these downland ridges all have their origins in the greensand and sandstone hills of the Weald. Thus the Rivers Wey, Mole, Darent, Medway and Stour have over the ages worn their routes through the North Downs on their northwards journeys to the Thames, while the Arun, Adur, Ouse and Cuckmere have cut through the South Downs to the English Channel.

The wildlife of these Wealden rivers naturally varies with the nature of the terrain through which they flow from their source to their mouth. Here, a brief account is given of the fauna and flora characteristic of them where they pass through the downland gaps or in their close vicinity. The fish just mentioned as occurring in the chalk streams are also to be found in these rivers and their tributaries; in addition there may be brook lampreys, the introduced North

American rainbow trout, pike, gudgeon, bleak, minnow, roach, chub, dace, stone loach and perch. Most of these prey on the invertebrate inhabitants of these rivers, such as freshwater shrimps, aquatic snails, water bugs and beetles and their larvae, dragonfly nymphs, mayflies and their nymphs (especially the so-called 'Green Drake' *Ephemera danica*), caddis-flies and stoneflies and their larvae, as well as the great variety of land insects which may fall in the water.

The River Darent near Shoreham, in Kent.

There are so many of these aquatic invertebrates that it becomes invidious to pick out any for special mention, especially when space is limited. But perhaps an exception should be made of the butterfly-like banded demoiselle damselfly. This beautiful insect, one of the dragonflies, which gets its name from the iridescent blue patches on each of the four wings of the male, has a metallic green body in both sexes. The female's wings, however, are entirely greenish; she does not fly as much as the male, who flutters with other males low over the water surface, hunting for smaller winged insects and on the look-out for females in a receptive state for mating. When he finds a female, he courts her by opening and closing his wings rhythmically, and raising and lowering his abdomen. Where the water is faster flowing, one may sometimes come across the banded demoiselle's larger relative, the beautiful demoiselle, in which the wings of the male are completely iridescent deep blue-violet and those of the female smoky brown. Adults of both species are on the wing on sunny days from late May to August over most of the downland rivers and streams.

89

Wild birds are, of course, greatly attracted by these rivers and their waterside habitats, and naturally include species which are not to be met with on the downlands above. Among the breeding species to be seen in spring and summer are the occasional pairs of little grebes, kingfishers, snipe, redshanks and yellow wagtails, while reed buntings and sedge warblers are often in plenty in the riverside vegetation, especially where there are reed-beds. A fine example of this river valley habitat is Amberley Wild (a corruption of 'Weald') Brooks, a large area of marshland intersected by dykes and ditches in the alluvial floodplain of the River Arun, near Pulborough, Sussex. Walkers on the South Downs Way above Amberley will see it spread out below them like a map. Although much of it is a Site of Special Scientific Interest, improvements to the drainage system in recent years have, unfortunately, led to it drying out; so it no

DEVILS KNEADINGTROUGH
WYE NATURE RESERVE 21st August

longer holds the immense numbers of teal, wigeon and other waterfowl which used to go there when winter flooding was much more frequent than it is now. Even so, good populations of wintering teal, wigeon, pochard and shoveler may be seen feeding on the water meadows, together with parties of pintail, Bewick's swans and occasional white-fronted geese.

Thanks to the Sussex Wildlife Trust, segments of the original and best habitats have been purchased and are being safeguarded. The Sussex Wildlife Trust also acquired about 43 hectares (106 acres) of the nearby Waltham Brooks, another area of marshy grazing pasture which links Amberley Wild Brooks with a similar area, Pulborough Brooks, to the north. Here, at Waltham Brooks, the marshland has become wetter and a large pool of standing water has formed. It, and the surrounding marsh pasture, has become

The Devil's Kneading Trough at Wye Down is a good example of an ancient river valley now dry.

91

an important wintering ground for Bewick's swans, shelduck, wigeon, teal, pochard and tufted ducks, while in the spring and autumn a wide variety of waders drop in to feed at the muddy margins of the pool. In the breeding season, redshank, snipe, lapwings, mallard, shelduck and yellow wagtails are among the species nesting there.

THE DOWNLAND HEATHS

Although the thick, uplifted layers of eroded chalk of the North and South Downs are mainly covered by thin calcareous soils with a characteristic chalk-loving (calcicolous) flora, this is not universally the case. Much of the dip slope on the north side of the North Downs and the south-facing dip slope of the South Downs is covered with large, scattered patches of clays, gravels and

sands. Large areas of the gentle dip slope and the rather flat crest of the North Downs are occupied by clay-with-flints overlying the chalk and here the ground is well wooded and thus accounts for the generally more wooded appearance of the North Downs compared with the South Downs. In those places where the soil is sandy the calcicolous flora is replaced by heathy vegetation, including such typical calcifuges (chalk-avoiding) as heather (ling), heaths, foxgloves, and heath bedstraw. Along the coastal stretches of the South Downs between Beachy Head and Seaford Head, Sussex, patches of reddish sands occur which are dominated by gorse and other plants that are not calcicoles.

Here and there, on both the North and South Downs, where the chalk is overlaid with superficial deposits of an acidic nature or where the hitherto chalky soil has been leached by rainwater gradually washing away its calcium carbonate content in solution, with the result that it has eventually become acidic, a 'chalk heath' flora has developed. Here typical heathland plants with

The chalky valley slopes at Magpie Bottom are rich in downland flowers including fragrant orchids and bird's-foot trefoil.

short roots like heather (ling), bell heather and heath bedstraw grow together with long-rooted chalk-loving plants and shrubs such as dropwort, salad burnet and spindle. One of the best examples of chalk heath is to be seen at Lullington Heath National Nature Reserve on the South Downs, between Eastbourne and Seaford. Another fine example is on the Sussex Wildlife Trust's reserve on Levin Down, near Chichester.

THE CHALK GRASSLAND FLORA

It is clear from the foregoing that the typical flora of chalk downland develops where there is a high lime (calcium carbonate) content in the soil. Where clay-with-flints or other superficial deposits occur on the dip slopes, as in Kent and Surrey, characteristic plants of the chalk need to be searched for in steep-sided, dry valleys carved out long ago by ancient streams which washed away the non-calcareous soils and exposed the chalk. But where highly calcareous grassland occurs, notably on the escarpment slopes, the chalk flora is seen at its best. In spite of the great losses to agriculture since the beginning of the Second World War and the decline of grazing by rabbits and sheep, fine stretches still exist along the escarpments of the North and South Downs, thanks, in no small measure, to the efforts of the former Nature Conservancy Council (now English Nature), the Countryside Commission, National Trust, county and local authorities, county wildlife trusts and other voluntary organizations. A good example is Wye and Crundale Downs National Nature Reserve on the North Downs between Ashford and Canterbury in Kent.

Apart from the beauty of many of the chalk flowers, the most obvious plants of chalk grassland are, of course, the dominant grasses. Some of these are highly adapted to calcareous soils and are rarely found on other soils. They include crested hair-grass, downy oat-grass, yellow oat-grass, mat-grass fescue, narrow-leaved meadow-grass, upright brome and tor grass. The perennial upright brome is the commonest tall grass of chalk grassland and, together with the locally abundant tor grass, often dominates those rough areas where grazing is absent or at a minimum. Tor grass, having a creeping habit, forms thick, conspicuous yellowish mats which crowd out most other plants. Its stiff, hair-fringed leaves are often yellow-green, sometimes with an orange hue, and it flowers from June to August, rather later than upright brome, which does so from May to July. Upright brome's flowers have orange anthers and a long bristle and are borne on purplish-green, long-stalked spikelets on erect, branched flower-heads. Its green leaves are usually hairless and provide nourishment for the caterpillars of the marbled white butterfly. Tor grass is a more popular larval foodplant among the butterflies, being eaten by the caterpillars of the Essex and large skippers, the marbled white, the meadow brown and the grayling.

Where the downland turf is grazed by sheep and/or rabbits and therefore kept short, the dominant grasses are usually fine grasses like sheep's fescue, red

Grazing by rabbits and sheep favours ground-hugging plants.

94

fescue, hair-grasses and oat-grasses which withstand close grazing well. Sheep's fescue is not confined to calcareous soils, but grows particularly well in dry grassland, such as is found on the downland slopes. It is a hairless, densely tufted grass with short, narrow, almost hair-like, waxy-green leaves which are eaten by the caterpillars of several downland butterflies: the grayling, marbled white, meadow brown, silver-spotted skipper, small heath and wall brown. Its greenish or purplish flower-heads appear towards the end of May and continue flowering into July. Red fescue, whose flowers appear in May and June and have shorter awns than sheep's fescue, also differs from that plant in its creeping habit and in possessing flat upper leaves. Like sheep's fescue it is not confined to calcareous soils and is as likely to be found in damp or even wet grassland as in dry grassland. It is not so popular as the sheep's fescue as a foodplant of butterfly larvae, but is known to be eaten by those of the gatekeeper or hedge brown, marbled white and grayling.

A very attractive and elegant grass which is bound to catch the attention of the downland rambler is the well-named quaking grass. Its shiny, oval or triangular-shaped green or purple-tinged spikelets, which hang downwards on long, slender stalks and dance in the slightest breeze, render it readily recognizable. Quaking grass flowers from May to August and is common almost everywhere on the North and South Downs. Other grasses, not confined to calcareous soils, which will be commonly met with on the downs of our region include false oat-grass, fern grass, false brome, cock's-foot, sweet vernal-grass, Yorkshire fog, crested dog's-tail, timothy grass, common couch and various species of bent and meadow-grass.

By mid-summer the variety of wild flowers characteristic of chalk grassland to be seen on the North and South Downs is extensive, and it is impossible to describe, even briefly, more than a few species here. The reader is referred for a more detailed account to the late J. E. Lousley's excellent book in the Collins' New Naturalist series *Wild Flowers of Chalk and Limestone*, originally published in 1950, and to the several very good guides to the British flora currently available. Among the characteristic species that you are certain to find on almost any stretch of chalk grassland on the North and South Downs are common rock-rose, horseshoe vetch, kidney vetch, fairy flax, squinancywort, yellow-wort, hoary plantain, marjoram, wild thyme, wild basil, eyebrights, red bartsia, clustered bellflower, dropwort, burnet-saxifrage, wild carrot, wild parsnip, field scabious, small scabious, black (lesser) knapweed, greater knapweed, dwarf (stemless) thistle, musk thistle and dark mullein.

Of these, the aromatic scent of such herbs as marjoram, wild basil and wild thyme is a distinctive feature of the downs in summer, and somewhat reminiscent of the south of France. Marjoram and wild thyme are relatives of the sweet marjoram and cultivated thyme used to flavour our food, but can be employed as substitutes, as can wild basil, although it is only a distant relative of the sweet basil grown in herb gardens (see Richard Mabey's book *Food for Free*). From July to September marjoram's clusters of many small purple-pink blossoms are very attractive to bees, butterflies, hover-flies and other nectar-seeking insects; so, too, are those of wild thyme which are also clustered together in reddish-purple flower-heads, only in this case, much denser and rounded. Wild thyme is, of course, much smaller than marjoram, having a low creeping habit and forming mats in the turf, especially on the nest hillocks of the yellow meadow ant. It flowers from May to August. Wild basil is quite different in appearance, being erect and bearing its rather large and bright, pink-purple flowers in whorls at the base of the uppermost leaves from July to September. They have a woolly appearance due to the white hairs which clothe the calyx and bristle-like bracts.

Another ubiquitous small-flowered wild plant of the downland turf is fairy flax, also called purging flax because of its former use as a purgative; it is, however, a violent purgative and potentially very poisonous. Fairy flax is slender and elegant, with small, paired leaves, and grows up to 25 cm (10 in) in height; it produces its many yellow-eyed, five-petalled white flowers from June to September. The unrelated squinancywort, a locally common bedstraw, has small flowers as well; but in this case they are pink and carried in terminal clusters on long stalks, also from June to September. Clustered bellflower, a stiff, very downy perennial with narrow bell-shaped, handsome purple-blue flowers, mainly densely clustered at the top of the plant, is very variable in height on the downs; it is locally common, depending upon the height of the grass. Where the turf is very short, dwarf plants may be found with only one or two blossoms and not a cluster; these may look like gentians. Clustered bellflowers will be found flowering from June to September. A rare relative of the last species in Britain, round-headed rampion, is locally plentiful on the North Downs in Surrey; however, it is more a speciality of the South Downs, where it is common in many localities. On the North Downs in Kent it is apparently extinct. An erect plant with broad basal leaves on long stalks and narrow unstalked leaves up the stem, round-headed rampion has dense, rounded flower-heads of beautiful Oxford-blue flowers. It can be seen in blossom in July and August in such places as around Box Hill, and on the escarpment below Ditchling Beacon, Sussex.

Dark mullein is one of the surest indicators of calcareous soil conditions and is therefore one of the most characteristic plants of the North and South Downs, where it is locally plentiful. It is easily distinguished from the common mullein by its many normally unbranched, often purple stems which arise from a rosette of basally heart-shaped leaves, and its deep-yellow flowers with orange stamens which have tufts of purple hairs attached to them.

Three species of umbellifers (carrot family) are especially characteristic of chalk grassland – wild carrot, wild parsnip and burnet-saxifrage – although none of them are confined to it. Wild parsnip has already been described in connection with arable chalk downs; the other two have white flowers instead of yellow ones and are both common almost everywhere on the North and South Downs. The large, dense and showy umbrella-like flower-heads of the wild carrot are the more conspicuous and are recognized by the ruff of long, downward-pointing, deeply divided leaf-like bracts beneath the flowerheads

The inner flowers, which possess petals of equal size, often have purplish-red centres, unlike the outer ones which lack them and which usually have petals of unequal size, the largest being on the outside and thus making the flower-head more conspicuous to a host of pollinating insects, including bees, wasps, and flies such as hover-flies. These insects also pollinate the smaller, daintier and less conspicuous flower-heads of burnet-saxifrage which lack the leafy, down-pointing bracts and appear in July, about a month later than those of wild carrot; although both continue flowering into early September. The lower leaves of burnet-saxifrage differ from the few, finely divided upper leaves and remind one of those of the unrelated plant, salad burnet. The upper leaves of wild carrot are also finer than the lower ones, but the resemblance to cultivated carrot is unmistakable.

One of the gems of chalk grassland is the distinctive and neat-looking yellow-wort. Its conspicuous terminal bright-yellow flowers contrast with the almost artificial-looking waxy grey-green pairs of triangular leaves completely surrounding the stem at regular intervals. It stands erect, up to 40 cm (16 in) high, and stands out amongst the adjacent vegetation. The flowers, which close quite early in the afternoon, blossom from late May into October, and may be seen in many parts of the North and South Downs.

Among the various thistles to be seen in blossom on the downs in summer are two species highly characteristic of calcareous soil – musk or nodding thistle and the 'picnicker's peril', dwarf or stemless thistle. The latter is very common throughout the North and South Downs and, because of its flat rosette of highly prickly leaves which hug the ground closely, it is easy not to notice it when you sink onto the inviting downland turf for a rest, only to rise again sharply. Dwarf thistle often spreads to form large patches to the exclusion of other plants and tolerates a great deal of trampling. Its attractive red-purple, usually stemless flower-heads may be seen from late June to September in most parts of the North and South Downs, and are a favourite nectar source for the now unfortunately rare and local silver-spotted skipper butterfly. Musk or nodding thistle is so called because its large (up to 6 cm ($2\frac{1}{2}$ in) diameter) and handsome solitary red-purple flower-heads droop and nod in the wind, and possess a delightful musk-like fragrance. They are pollinated by many nectar-seeking insects, including not only several species of bee, but also burnet and forester moths, and a variety of different butterflies, during their long flowering period from May to September, or even later. Apart from its bright flowers, musk thistle is a grey, cottony-looking plant with prickly leaves and spiny wings on the stems; and is usually locally plentiful throughout the North and South Downs, especially where the grassland turf has been disturbed. Thistles, generally, produce great quantities of thistledown – light seeds with long hairs (pappus) which float in the wind and are thus widely dispersed. These are a favourite food of goldfinches and linnets at this time, and parties of adults and juveniles of both species may be met with on the downs, perching on the thistle-heads and so engrossed in their feast that a quiet observer may approach them quite closely. And, however uninviting the spiny foliage of thistles may seem to us, it affords nourishment for the caterpillars of the lovely painted lady butterfly, a regular immigrant to Britain from the Mediterranean region.

Scabiouses also provide splendid nectar refuelling stations for a wide range of insects, including butterflies and moths. Two species are common and widespread on the downs: field scabious and small scabious, both producing their blue-violet flowers from June to September. The former is by no means confined to calcareous grassland, but small scabious is largely so and is a very good indicator of limy soil. It is smaller and more slender than field scabious, although some plants may grow as high as 70 cm (28 in) compared with the field scabious's maximum of about a metre (3 ft).

Dropwort, a small relative of the familiar and fragrant meadowsweet of damp situations, is an attractive plant entirely confined to calcareous grasslands: it is, therefore, another good indicator of lime. It has fewer, but bigger and unscented, creamy-white flowers tinged with reddish pink on the underside; these may be seen flowering in plenty in many dry and sunny places on the North and South Downs from May to August, although there are gaps; for example on the Kentish chalk near London. Common rock-rose is yet another good indicator of calcareous soil in the south of England, being largely confined to it. It is locally common on grassy downland slopes throughout the North and South Downs, where its bright-yellow, five-petalled flowers, 2–2.5 cm (1 in) in diameter, first appear in May and continue blossoming well into September. The plant itself is a low, more or less prostrate, undershrub which grows in loose-looking mats.

Two vetches, horseshoe vetch and kidney vetch, are especially characteristic of calcareous grassland and are foodplants of, respectively, the adonis blue and the small blue butterflies. Kidney vetch is not entirely confined to calcareous soil, but horseshoe vetch certainly is and is therefore another very good indicator. Both have yellow flowers, typical of the pea family to which they belong, and may be found in blossom from May to July in the case of the horseshoe vetch, and from May to as late as September in the kidney vetch. Those of the latter are crowded together in a rounded flower-head, while the horseshoe vetch flowers are spaced out in a half-circle of five to eight at the top of long stalks. The name 'horseshoe vetch' is derived from the fanciful resemblance of the wavy seed-pods to horseshoes joined together; 'kidney vetch' is so called because of its reputed medicinal properties. Both species are locally common throughout the North and South Downs.

SUMMER BUTTERFLIES AND MOTHS OF THE DOWNS

The horseshoe vetch is not only the sole foodplant of the adonis blue butterfly, but normally of its close relative, the chalk-hill blue, as well. Both species of butterfly are confined to calcareous grassland and often occur together in the same areas, but seem to avoid ecological competition by appearing in their

John Dev..
12th August Levin Do..

various stages of development at different times of the year. Thus adonis blue adults appear on the wing in May and June, and again, as a second generation, in August and September, whereas the adults of the chalk-hill blue only fly from July to early September. Therefore, only the adonis second generation overlaps to some extent; but as the eggs of the chalk-hill blue laid at this time do not hatch until the following March or April, whereas those of the adonis blue's second generation already hatch in September or early in October, the caterpillars feeding until they hibernate for the winter, there is no competition between them for food. Moreover, when they awake and resume feeding in March, they are well ahead of the chalk-hill blue caterpillars in their development, which are only just hatching. The latter, furthermore, feed only at dusk and by night, unlike the adonis blue caterpillars which are daytime feeders. So even though the larvae of both species may feed on the same individual plants they are not directly competing, a good example of ecological segregation.

By late April the adonis blue first-brood caterpillars are fully grown and ready to pupate on the ground, anchored by a few silken strands. Thereafter, they are usually discovered by ants, chiefly *Lasius alienus* and *Myrmica sabuleti*, and buried by them in a chamber connected to their nest by an underground passage, and constantly tended and milked by up to ten ants at a time for a sweet secretion they produce. The perfect butterfly emerges after some twenty days in this stage. The caterpillars of both broods are also continuously tended by ants while feeding in the daytime, and are buried each night by them in an earthen cell where they rest or, when necessary, moult their old skin. The caterpillars of the first generation of butterflies hatch in June and pupate a month later, the pupae being attended in the same way by ants. When stimulated by the ants with their antennae, the adonis blue caterpillars exude the sweet, honey-like secretion from a gland and scattered pores on their body.

Chalk-hill blues also have these pores and honey gland, and are tended just as industriously by ants of the same species as the adonis blue, plus the yellow meadow ant *Lasius flavus*, when they feed at dusk and during the night. During the day they rest at the base of horseshoe vetch, but may be temporarily buried by the ants which continue to attend them and seek their secretions. This association between ants and the larvae of adonis and chalk-hill blues appears to be symbiotic, in that the larvae receive protection by the ants from predators in exchange for a source of nourishment. As with the adonis blue, the chalk-hill blue pupae, too, exude sweet secretions appreciated by the ants, and are buried by them and constantly attended and milked until the adult butterflies emerge some 30 days after pupating.

Both adonis and chalk-hill blues have suffered from the ploughing of their downland habitats since the Second World War and from the decline of rabbit and sheep grazing since the mid-1950s; the former having lost proportionately the greatest number of colonies. By 1981 not more than 70–80 adonis blue colonies, half of them in Dorset, were thought to exist throughout its English range which is restricted to south-eastern England. Since then, however, successful management of surviving suitable habitats by increasing grazing and

Chalk-hill blue butterflies on marjoram, together with meadow brown and large skipper butterflies.

ORCHIDS

As described on pages 84–5, the southern chalk hills, particularly those of the North and South Downs, are rich in both their variety and numbers of wild orchids. The ten species depicted on the opposite page are all more or less common there, except for the frog orchid, and are arranged in the date order in which John Davis painted them.

The early purple orchid, as its name suggests, is a truly spring-flowering orchid, starting well before most of the others. Not confined to calcareous soils, it can often be found in southern woods blossoming among the carpets of bluebells from April until June, and occasionally amid downland scrub.

The unobtrusive fly orchid is so called because of the resemblance of its flowers to large flies. It is in bloom in May and June in shady, grassy places along wood borders and amongst scrub.

The numerous, relatively large white flowers of the greater butterfly orchid do look rather butterfly-like: they are conspicuous after dark and their sweet scent attracts night-flying moths. These blossoms should be looked for in the downland woods and also amongst scrub in June and July.

The fragrant orchid is another sweet-scented orchid which flowers in June and July and is attractive to butterflies as well as moths. It grows in open grassy places.

The single pair of broad, pointed leaves which arise opposite each other at the base of the long slender flower spike give the common twayblade its name. The widely spaced, inconspicuous greenish-yellow flowers appear from May to July. It will be found quite commonly in beech and other downland woods.

The bee orchid is very aptly named, and the reason for the form of its flower is explained on page 85. Flowering in June and July, it is locally common in downland turf where it grows at its best in longer grass.

The pyramidal orchid is yet another scented orchid which attracts butterflies and moths to seek its nectar and thus pollinate it. It often grows in profusion in the downland turf where its distinctive pyramid-shaped flower-heads, densely packed with individual blossoms, attract attention.

One of the commonest orchids, the common spotted orchid thrives not only on the chalk downs, but on various other non-acid soils, including the marshy pastures of the river valleys cutting through the downs. It blooms from late May to August and is pollinated by various bees and flies.

Another small, unobtrusive orchid that can easily be overlooked among the grasses in the downland turf where it blooms from June to August is the frog orchid. It is locally frequent on the South Downs, but much rarer on the North Downs.

As its name indicates, autumn lady's-tresses is a late summer and early autumn-flowering orchid whose spiralling blossoms, as the illustration shows, remind one of the plaited tresses of ladies' hair-styles of long ago. More will be found about this graceful plant on pages 125–7.

by the reintroduction of populations to former sites has led to a recovery of around 150 colonies – a great achievement by nature conservationists.

The adonis blue, whose brilliant blue males (the females are brown) make it one of our most beautiful butterflies, needs short-turf calcareous grassland to survive, perhaps because its chief associated ants *Myrmica sabuleti* and *Lasius alienus* thrive best in such conditions. However, it is very sensitive to apparently minor changes in its habitat and, although it requires turf less than 3 cm (1⅛ in) in height, it has been demonstrated that extreme over-grazing can also affect it adversely. Colonies thrive best on steep and sunny south-facing slopes, but are subject to remarkably wide fluctuations in population size; these usually depend upon the effect of annual variations in the weather, such as droughts or prolonged wet springs. Although some of its colonies are large in good years, the adonis blue is still very local and vulnerable nowadays in England, including the North and South Downs. Fortunately, some of the strongest colonies exist on nature reserves managed by English Nature and the Kent, Surrey, Hampshire and Sussex wildlife conservation trusts. Examples apart from Old Winchester Hill, Hampshire, are Lydden and Queendown (Kent), Colekitchen, Gomshall (Surrey), and Castle Hill and Malling Down (East Sussex).

The chalk-hill blue, the males of which have silver-blue upperwings, is more tolerant of minor or relatively minor changes in its habitat than the adonis blue, so long as its larval foodplant, horseshoe vetch, survives in sufficient quantity on slopes which receive enough sunshine. The chalk-hill blue is, in fact, able to tolerate longer turf than the adonis blue, provided the horseshoe vetch is not shaded out. It is still locally common along the North and South Downs where suitable habitat remains, including the nature reserves just listed in respect of the adonis blue. It, too, prefers sunny south-facing slopes and on some of these it may be abundant, although its numbers can fluctuate markedly from year to year, but not usually as severely as in the case of the adonis blue. The adult butterflies of both species visit the blossoms of various downland flowers for nectar, including those of horseshoe vetch, eyebright, marjoram, knapweeds, scabiouses and various thistles.

Another butterfly confined to calcareous soils in southern England, which has always been local and has become even more localized for the same reasons as the adonis and chalk-hill blues, is the silver-spotted skipper. It is the same size as the common and widely distributed large skipper, and looks very similar to it, except for the greenish undersides of the hindwings which are spotted with distinctive silver-white spots – hence its name. At the present time the silver-spotted skipper is only found on the North and South Downs on closely grazed, sparse turf, usually on south-facing slopes, along the escarpment of the North Downs between Guildford and Reigate in Surrey, and in east Kent, plus a very few sites on the South Downs in Sussex and in east Hampshire, including the National Nature Reserve of Old Winchester Hill. Outside this area it is now only known from a few places on the chalk in the Chiltern Hills, Dorset, north Hampshire and Wiltshire, and one locality on limestone in Somerset. The adult butterflies fly at great speed only in hot sunny weather (20°C +) from late July to early September, and take nectar from such wild flowers as dwarf (stemless) thistle, carline thistle, hawkweeds, knapweeds, field scabious, small scabious and autumn gentian (felwort). They also spend much time basking in sunspots on the ground, but generally roost at night on adjacent flower-heads, scrub or even trees. The females deposit their pearl-white, upside-down pudding basin-shaped eggs deep in small isolated tussocks of the larval foodplant, sheep's fescue grass, beside bare pieces of ground, such as scrapes made by rabbits. They ignore dense swards of the grass, even if this has been grazed short. The caterpillars hatch the following March and spin a silken tent between the lower leaves of the sheep's fescue, emerging at night to feed on the adjacent leaves. They are usually ready to pupate in July, which they do in a flimsy silk cocoon strengthened with grass blades and spun very low down in the grass tussock. The silver-spotted skipper benefits from intense grazing from rabbits, so the recovery of the population of this mammal in many areas in recent years and the effects of careful management on the nature reserves and National Trust land where more than half of the known colonies occur, have facilitated an improvement in the butterfly's fortunes in some of its sites.

Among summer butterflies characteristic of the chalk downlands, but not confined to them, are the brown argus, dark green fritillary, marbled white and grayling. The first generation of adults of the brown argus is on the wing in May and June; its second generation flies from late July to mid-September and overwinters in the caterpillar stage, resting motionless underneath a leaf until it is time to wake up in late March. The large and handsome dark green fritillary is another butterfly which has suffered from agricultural 'improvement' of its grassland haunts and the invasion of some of those on the chalk downs by scrub. Despite this it is still locally common on the slopes, especially the steeper ones, of the North and South Downs, where it flies powerfully and rapidly on sunny days from late June until the end of August, pausing only to take nectar from dwarf and other thistles, field scabious, knapweeds and red clover. Its chief larval foodplant on calcareous soil, hairy violet, must, of course, be present, although occasionally the common dog-violet is utilized. The dark green fritillary is not so dependent upon short turf as any of the previous species, preferring a lightly or infrequently grazed mosaic of short to long grass where violets can flourish.

The marbled white actually requires long grass with a varied mixture of species and a degree of shelter from hedgerows or scattered scrub. On such unimproved downland it is often numerous on the Hampshire Downs, along most of the South Downs and at the western and eastern ends of the North Downs. Despite its name and unmistakable black and white chequer-board pattern, the marbled white is not related to the 'white' butterflies, but to the family of 'browns' (the Satyridae). It flies from late June to the middle of August, but may occasionally be met with later. The adults fly in a rather leisurely manner, but are deceptively fast if disturbed. They spend a lot of time feeding at flowers, including brambles, knapweeds, scabiouses, thistles, wild privet, pyramidal orchid and marjoram.

The grayling is a more typical member of the 'brown' family of butterflies, at least as far as its general colour and eyespots go. Those living on calcareous soils are paler than the dark, more richly coloured butterflies occurring on heathland, and tend to have a whiter irregular band through the middle of the hindwings, which may be quite indistinct in some heathland individuals. The chalk form used to be widely distributed and locally common along the North and South Downs, but since the 1950s it has declined and/or disappeared from many of its former haunts, especially in Kent and Surrey. It is, however, still locally common on the Hampshire and South Downs wherever open short-grazed turf exists. It is the lack of close grazing, particularly by rabbits following the arrival of myxomatosis, that seems to have been chiefly responsible for the decline on the downlands. Now that rabbits are returning there are also signs that the grayling may be returning as well, as it is in Kent.

Graylings may be seen in characteristically erratic flight from early July to the middle of September. When alighting, usually on the ground, they display for a moment or two above the closed hindwings the conspicuous eye-spots on the forewing tips. Should a nearby predator, such as a bird or lizard, launch a sudden attack, its aim would most likely be directed at the eyespots and away from the vulnerable parts of the insect, thus allowing its escape with the loss of only an expendable piece of wing. If no attack is made, the forewings are withdrawn from sight below the camouflaged hindwings which make concealment almost complete, but not quite. The butterfly then tilts to one side, towards the sun, thus reducing the size of its shadow and making it extremely difficult to see, and at the same time regulating its body temperature on hot days. On downland the females lay their eggs on sheep's fescue and other fine-leaved grasses, on which the caterpillars feed at night from late summer or autumn (even, when mild, in the winter) till early the following June.

As well as butterflies, there are a number of moths that are especially characteristic of chalk downland; some of which, like the cistus and scarce foresters, chalk carpet and straw belle, are entirely confined to calcareous soils. Indeed, a few species are actually unknown in Britain away from the North and South Downs. However, the moths most likely to catch the eye of the casual rambler on the downs are three species of burnets, which, because of their striking crimson-spotted and blue-black colours and day-flying habit, usually cause the non-naturalist to assume that they are butterflies. They will be encountered in considerable numbers during the summer, several often crowding the flower-heads of a single thistle, knapweed or field scabious. In bright sunshine all fly rather heavily and slowly in a whirr of crimson as the hindwings, hidden by the forewings at rest, are revealed. When imbibing nectar, which they do from a wide variety of downland flowers, they appear quite unconcerned and not easily alarmed. Their apparent lack of fear of attack is due to their complete reliance upon their toxicity. When attacked by, for example, a bird, they release very small drops of a yellowish fluid from glands on the back containing hydrocyanic acid (prussic acid), which cause their instant rejection. Having thus had the misfortune to taste one of these moths, an assailant remembers the distinctive red and black colour pattern, and thereafter avoids them and other similarly colour-patterned insects.

The three species to be found on the North and South Downs are the five-spot burnet, which flies in late May and June; the narrow-bordered five-spot burnet, flying in late June and July; and the six-spot burnet, flying from late June to August. The latter two species are not restricted to calcareous downland, but the subspecies *palustrella* of the five-spot burnet is, occurring only along the North and South Downs from Kent and East Sussex to Hampshire, where it is widespread and locally common, and on Salisbury Plain and in the south Cotswolds. There is also a marshland subspecies, *decreta*, found in the west of Britain, which is now thought to be extinct in south-east England. The larvae of this subspecies feed on greater bird's-foot trefoil, whereas those of the chalk downland subspecies and the narrow-bordered five-spot and six-spot feed only bird's-foot trefoil.

The forester moths are allied to the burnets and are similar in general form and appearance, except that they are smaller and have metallic-green forewings and greyish hindwings. Of the three British species, the common forester lives in various habitats, including chalk downs, and is locally common throughout the North and South Downs. The other two, the cistus and scarce foresters are confined to calcareous soils, the cistus being locally plentiful on the North and South Downs, while the scarce forester is much more local, and is currently known only from Salisbury Plain and the Sussex downs between Findon and Eastbourne, although it used to be found on the downs of south-east Kent. All three fly on sunny days in June and July and feed from a variety of downland flowers, including knapweeds, scabiouses, thistles, salad burnet, rock-rose, wild thyme, trefoils and clovers. The caterpillars of the common forester feed on sorrels, the cistus forester on common rock-rose and the scarce forester on black or lesser knapweed and greater knapweed – all from July to May.

Summer night-flying moths characteristic of the chalk which are more or less widespread and plentiful on the North and South Downs include such species as the small emerald and pretty chalk carpet (both have caterpillars which feed on traveller's joy), chalk carpet (larvae on clovers and trefoils), pimpinel pug (larvae in seed-capsules of burnet-saxifrage), broad-barred white (larvae on hawk's-beards and hawkweeds), royal mantle and small elephant hawk (larvae of both species on bedstraws). All, except the broad-barred white and the small elephant hawk, although naturally night-flying, are easily seen in the daytime as they fly readily when disturbed, especially the chalk carpet.

GRASSHOPPERS AND BUSH-CRICKETS

Next to the Hampshire Basin area, the counties of Kent, Surrey and Sussex are the richest areas in the British Isles for the essentially warmth-loving bush-crickets and grasshoppers. The following species are more or less common throughout the North and South Downs: the oak, great green, dark and speckled bush-crickets, the common groundhopper, and the stripe-winged, woodland, common green, field, meadow and mottled grasshoppers. Of these, the stripe-winged, woodland and mottled grasshoppers are characteristic of chalk downland, although not restricted to it. This is also true of some much more localized species like the long-winged conehead bush-cricket and the rufous grasshopper. All, except for the common groundhopper, stripe-winged, field and mottled grasshoppers, seem to have benefited from reduced grazing of the downland turf since the 1950s, and the consequent development of coarser, longer grasses and herbage.

The long-winged conehead, a small, emerald-green bush-cricket with a brown back and wings, inhabits rough grassland and vegetation all along the South Downs westwards from Lullington and Telscombe Cliffs in East Sussex to the Isle of Purbeck in Dorset. Until 1990 the long-winged conehead was not known to occur on the North Downs, but, as a result of an intermittent series of hot summers since the mid-1970s, it has undergone a population explosion and expansion. It has spread northwards through Hampshire and Surrey, where it was located just south of the North Downs at Elstead, then on the North Downs themselves at Bookham Common. No doubt further searches will reveal its presence elsewhere on the North Downs, as has already been the case on the northern slopes of the South Downs.

The rufous grasshopper is easily recognized from other true grasshoppers by its white-tipped, clubbed antennae, like those of a butterfly. The only other British grasshopper with clubbed antennae is the mottled grasshopper, which is also found on the chalk downs, but this is smaller and lacks the white tips. The rufous grasshopper is a local calcareous grassland species in England, being most common along the North Downs from the Hog's Back in Surrey to Wye Downs and Folkestone Warren in Kent. On the South Downs it is locally common in West Sussex from Kingley Vale National Nature Reserve to Arundel Park, but has never been discovered east of the River Arun. In Hampshire there are isolated colonies on Noar Hill Nature Reserve, near Selborne, and on Old Winchester Hill National Nature Reserve, among others. The mottled grasshopper, on the other hand, is usually common on exposed soil with sparse short turf wherever this occurs on the North and South Downs, including the chalk heaths. The stripe-winged grasshopper also favours this type of habitat and its presence is considered to be a good indicator of old, species-rich calcareous turf. It is locally plentiful throughout the North and South Downs, and the Hampshire Downs. The woodland grasshopper, the mature males of which are black with largely bright-red abdomens and white-tipped palps, is much more local, and mainly confined to wide grassy rides and clearings in the downland woods or in adjacent grassland with scattered bushes. It is, nevertheless, often quite common within its range and is found in a considerable number of localities scattered along the North and South Downs from Hampshire to East Kent.

Grasshoppers, bush-crickets and crickets are associated in the mind with high summer; this is because that is the period in Britain when most species mature and are then able to 'sing', thus attracting our attention. Their singing is, of course, not vocal, but instrumental and is strictly called 'stridulation'. Each species produces a distinct song and, with practice, entomologists can identify them by this means in the same way that ornithologists recognize birds by their songs and calls. Unfortunately, as one ages it becomes more and more difficult to hear the high-pitched sounds of the bush-crickets.

Fortunately for those of us with normal hearing it is possible, though, to hear the cheerful chirping of a colony of field-crickets even at the age of 60 or more. Sadly, this once locally plentiful insect, so familiar to Gilbert White at Selborne in the eighteenth century, has virtually disappeared since then from England. It is now confined to West Sussex, where one colony is known – the one on the well-known downland cricket ground at Arundel died out in 1988. It used to be more widespread in Sussex, and in Hampshire and Surrey too, but has gradually disappeared since the Second World War, partly as a result of habitat destruction, but more probably because of subtle climatic changes. Field-crickets mature earlier than bush-crickets and grasshoppers do in the English climate, with the result that the males may be heard chirping much of the day and night at the entrances to their burrows as early as May; they carry on doing so throughout the spring and summer into July. Their song is very similar to that of the house-cricket; however, except in particularly hot summers, that species is only likely to be heard out-of-doors in warm compost heaps and rubbish dumps.

AUTUMN

Autumn, in the opinion of many people, is the most beautiful of the seasons – a season of rich colour and plenty before the leaves fall from the deciduous trees and the shortages and starkness of winter slowly set in. The downlands of southern England are among the loveliest parts of Britain at this time, their yellow-green grassy slopes flanked with the golden-brown of the beech-woods while the now colourful scrub is bright with vast quantities of berries of various shades of red – hawthorn, spindle, whitebeam, bryonies and dog rose.

A major feature of interest in the downland at this time of year is the departure of summer birds. Cuckoos and swifts are the first birds to depart for warmer climes. The adult cuckoos depart in August, before the juveniles of that year's breeding season; the latter linger on until about mid-September before following the route south to Africa taken by their parents. Thus they lack their parents' guidance, but instinctively know the way, having inherited it with their genes. Swifts, young and old, leave their breeding sites by late August; but some will still be seen pausing to feed over downland rivers as late as late September as they drift south together to their winter quarters in West Africa.

The superficially similar hirundines – swallows, house martins and sand martins – leave later than the swifts. The sand martins are the first of them to depart, gathering in large flocks as early as July prior to their flight south. However, their main passage occurs throughout August and September, and even into October. Sand martins winter in the Sahel region on the southern edge of the Sahara, but owing to the increasing desertification of this semi-arid area during the 1960s and 1970s they have suffered higher winter mortality than was formerly the case; consequently the European breeding populations have been much depleted.

A juvenile kestrel keeping watch at the top of an old yew tree.

Swallows may also begin assembling in July and August, but their main migratory movements take place in September and continue into October. House martins follow much the same pattern although their main autumn movements occur in late September and well into October in the south. Since some pairs may rear as many as three broods, adults and juveniles may be seen at breeding sites in September or even later in downland towns and villages. However, migrating house martins which have spent the summer further north have

111

a tendency to visit other nests of their own species en route, so making the observer think that the local birds are still present or have temporarily returned.

Hobby falcons, themselves summer residents, also migrate to Africa and frequently follow the southward-moving flocks of martins and swallows on which they prey. At such times we can marvel at their speed and dexterity as they pick out and then swoop on their fast-flying victims.

In the trees and bushes below, many other bird migrants are moving too, although, as they move in a slow, leisurely way, spending much of their time feeding, this may not be obvious to the human observer. They include various species of warblers, flycatchers, nightingales, redstarts, tree pipits and other small passerines whose migratory flights take place at night. By day they move from bush to bush or tree to tree, alternately feeding and resting; preparing for

the exertion of the night flight. Most numerous of the migrant warblers on the downs are the chiffchaffs and willow warblers. So indistinguishable are they, so far as plumage characteristics are concerned, that bird-watchers lump them together as 'willow/chiffs'. In fact, if one gets close enough the chiffchaff's dark, blackish legs distinguish it from the willow warbler's paler brown legs; but it is by no means an infallible field character and much depends upon the quality of the light at the time. Sometimes, male chiffchaffs reveal their identity by singing their distinctive jerky song in the autumn; whereas willow warblers rarely, if ever, sing their melodious and completely different cadence at that time.

During autumn species not normally associated with the southern down-lands might well be seen, such as pied flycatchers, ring ouzels and wheatears en route to the coast from more northerly uplands where they breed. The ring

Redstart, and migrant hirundines on Old Winchester Hill, Hampshire, gather before returning to their winter quarters.

ouzels and wheatears will, of course, be encountered on more open downlands, especially the latter species, which can also be seen in the river valley fields. Until the introduction of bird protection laws put an end to it earlier this century, large numbers of migrating wheatears, plump with the fat reserves built up for their impending flight across the English Channel, used to be trapped on the South Downs by bird-catchers and sent to the local markets,

This ring ouzel is feeding up on berries before making the long journey back to its winter quarters.

where they were sold as a delicacy. Gilbert White described in the eighteenth century how the shepherds near Lewes used to supplement their income handsomely by trapping 'vast quantities' which he reported were sent for sale to Brighthelmstone (Brighton) and Tunbridge (Wells), and appeared 'at the tables of all the gentry that entertain with any degree of elegance'. Before this trade ceased, the Victorian naturalist W. H. Hudson was able to give a graphic account of it in his book *Nature in Downland*.

Gilbert White regularly saw migrating ring ouzels during his autumn visits to the South Downs over a period of more than thirty years. He mentions seeing them for two to three weeks from the end of September into October, feeding on haws and yew berries, in small parties scattered about the Sussex Downs all the way from Chichester to Lewes. He found them to be completely unafraid of men with guns. In mid-April they passed through again on their way north, but only stayed for about a week, feeding on ivy berries. This migration pattern is much the same today although the ring ouzel is far less commonly seen west of the River Arun than in White's day, and has declined throughout its breeding range in north and west Britain since about 1900.

Of course, ring ouzels can be seen on spring and autumn passage almost anywhere on the North Downs as well. However, they seem to be easier to see on the more open South Downs, especially in the east and in autumn when they tend to concentrate near the coast before leaving on their perilous night flights over the sea to the European mainland. In other downland areas, ring ouzels are more easily overlooked among the denser woods and scrub, and some bird-watchers are more alert to them than others. It has been suggested, however, that many of these autumn birds on the coast are Scandinavian ring ouzels which have strayed across the Channel in adverse weather while migrating south-westwards across the North Sea.

As well as ring ouzels, all the birds mentioned so far will be encountered on autumn (and spring) passage on all the southern downlands in suitable habitats. Nevertheless, like the ring ouzel, they will usually be seen in greater numbers along the south coast as they 'pile up', waiting for the right weather conditions under which to make the sea-crossing. A good place to see such concentrations of migrant passerines is at Beachy Head, near Eastbourne. It has become the most important place in Sussex for studying migration, and an observatory has been established nearby at Whitebread Hollow. In September it is an ideal place to watch the massive daytime movements of swallows and other hirundines, and finches, larks and pipits in October.

AUTUMN MOVEMENTS OF BUTTERFLIES AND MOTHS

Birds are not the only migrants to be seen along the southern coast of England. The naturalist watching hirundines flying out over the chalk cliffs of Beachy Head and elsewhere in September and early October may also see migrating summer butterflies leaving southwards too: painted ladies, red admirals, clouded yellows, large whites, small whites and perhaps other species. Occasionally they might be seen in swarms, but more usually they drift by in ones and twos, spread out over a broad front. After Atlantic gales in September and early October he or she may be lucky to see a monarch butterfly glide in, a large and magnificent North American species, which is sometimes swept off course by the autumn gales from its migration route south down the eastern seaboard of North America, and carried by them right across the Atlantic to the coasts of Europe, especially the British Isles. The autumn of 1968 had seen, with 63 recorded, the biggest influx of monarchs ever before recorded in the British Isles; but it was exceeded by that of 1981 when 135 monarchs were reported. In recent years occasional individuals have been seen on the South Downs; as recently as 15 August 1989 one was observed at close range feeding from buddleia at Jevington, near Eastbourne.

At night, when warblers, flycatchers and other nocturnal migrant birds are flying out over the sea, many other migrants arrive on the southern coasts. These are moths, of a variety of species, flying here from the continental mainland. A great deal still needs to be learned about the patterns of these movements and why they fly westwards or northwards to English shores at a time when most other migrants, birds and insects, are flying in the opposite directions. They seem, in most cases, to be dispersal movements from their main European breeding areas rather than true migrations like the regular north and south flights of birds. Moreover, the numbers and diversity of species are unpredictable and vary from year to year. The commonest include the dark sword-grass, pearly underwing, common yellow underwing, silver y and rush veneer. Among the less common are the death's head hawk-moth, convolvulus hawk-moth, bedstraw hawk-moth, silver-striped hawk-moth, white-speck, white-point, the delicate, small mottled willow, scarce silver y, dark bordered straw, scarce bordered straw, the gem and the vestal.

Some species, like the common yellow underwing and the angle shades, are resident in the British Isles, but their numbers are greatly augmented in autumn by immigrants. Our knowledge of the times of arrival, distribution pattern and numbers depends to a considerable extent upon the many lepidopterists who regularly operate light traps, usually in their gardens, especially around our southern coasts. After the night's catch is identified and recorded, the moths are released by their captors in the safety and security of the adjacent shrubberies or other thick vegetation. From such observations we know that the largest numbers and greatest diversity of species usually arrive in September and October, sometimes continuing into November.

According to the late Mr R. F. Bretherton, who was one of the foremost authorities on the migrations of Lepidoptera in the British Isles, the greatest

Amberley Wild Brooks is a rich marshy floodplain visited by many waders and other waterfowl, where snipe and lapwings breed.

Amberley Wild Brooks 4th October John Davis '91

numbers of species and individuals probably reach us from the south-west: north Africa, Spain or from the Mediterranean area through France. Some travel the short distance across the English Channel from the coasts of France and Belgium, while others cross the North Sea, probably mainly from Scandinavia. As we have seen, the monarch butterfly makes it across the Atlantic from North America, and so very occasionally does the American painted lady butterfly and such moths as Stephen's gem and the beautiful utethesia. Other, subtropical, moths may come from the African Atlantic islands of the Azores, Canaries and Madeira. More rarely some immigrants may originate in eastern Europe, Siberia or even elsewhere in Asia. For example there is evidence that influxes of bedstraw hawk-moths in the southern half of England in the summers of 1972 and 1973 originated in the southern Ukraine.

Such migrations may start through dispersal from areas of over-population or because of some special circumstances, such as drought in the breeding areas. The insects may then drift for long distances on strong winds, having perhaps been caught up in them by upward convection currents. As with those birds which have drifted off their normal migration routes because of strong winds,

the insects may subsequently try to reorientate themselves, but have little chance of regaining their original haunts. Wind-drifted insects may well be carried along for several days, and, on landing, will be in urgent need of refreshment to replenish their lost fat and sugar. Thus, newly arrived migrants will be seen feeding eagerly from nectar-yielding flowers.

One of the late Mr Bretherton's experiences was of a swarm of many hundreds of silver y moths which suddenly arrived at 9.30 p.m. one autumn night at an illuminated sheet he had set up above a Sussex beach, and stayed for an hour before taking off and flying on, leaving hardly any of their number behind. The silver y, which occurs over much of the northern half of the world, is usually one of the most abundant of the autumn immigrants to Britain. It is a medium-sized, dark, but beautifully patterned moth with a distinctive silvery mark, shaped like a hand-written letter 'y', in the centre of each of its forewings; from this it gets its familiar English name, and also its scientific name of *Autographa gamma* because of the likeness as well to the Greek letter *gamma*. Very few, if any, survive the British winters, and therefore it is only able to maintain itself here by annual immigration. In some years they can be relatively

Ivy blossom provides by day and night a rich source of nectar for insects in the autumn when there are few other flowers in bloom.

scarce, but every two or three years large numbers of immigrants arrive and the early ones give rise to a large British-bred population. In certain years the moth is exceptionally numerous and migrant swarms may appear, as in 1936, 'in such great numbers that the sound of their wings was audible as distinct humming'.

Although typically a night flyer, the silver y will fly by day as well when on migration. Scientists at the Rothamsted Experimental Station at Harpenden, Hertfordshire, have demonstrated that the migratory urge overcomes its natural reluctance to fly in the daytime, thus enabling it to undertake migratory journeys in a shorter time than would be the case if they rested during the daylight hours. At night, silver y moths are attracted by artificial light and often whirr in through open windows to the consternation of the room occupants; so they are readily caught in light traps. In addition to imbibing nectar from daytime flowers, they feed avidly at night-flowering plants. Therefore ivy-blossom attracts them, as well as many other insects by day and night.

IVY BLOSSOM — A VITAL INSECT RESOURCE

Ivy blossom is, in fact, one of the most important wild sources of nectar available to insects in the autumn; not only on the downlands, but wherever this widely distributed climbing plant grows. The nectaries of ivy flowers are well exposed and therefore easily exploited by a wide range of short-tongued insects, such as bees, wasps, drone-flies, hover-flies, bluebottles, blow-flies and even caddis flies. These and butterflies, like the comma, peacock and red admiral, in the daytime and various moths at night feed from them so avidly that they often become intoxicated and drowsy. Some of these species will die before the onset of winter, leaving only their eggs or larvae to perpetuate them; but others are storing up fat reserves to see them through the winter hibernation. By the time the ivy blossom is over in November they will have sought out sleeping quarters in such places as hollow trees, under bark, in outhouses, in bunches of dead leaves or amongst the evergreen foliage of the ivy itself. They include moths with intriguing names such as the buttoned snout, the chestnut, dotted chestnut, grey shoulder-knot, the herald, orange upper-wing, the satellite and tawny pinion.

Not all the moths which visit ivy flowers hibernate through the winter as adults; a few, like the silver y, may, as we have seen, migrate south; but the majority perish as winter weather arrives. Among these may be mentioned such species as the angle shades, the sallow, barred sallow, centre-barred sallow, pink-barred sallow, beaded chestnut, lunar underwing, red-line quaker and rosy rustic. With the exception of the angle shades and lunar underwing, all of these overwinter in the egg stage; the two exceptions as larvae. The caterpillars of the lunar underwing feed in a leisurely manner through the winter on various grasses, like annual meadow-grass, cock's-foot and Yorkshire fog, until ready to pupate in the soil in May. The angle shades is something of a special case which has not yet been fully studied; some of the adults seen in autumn may survive the winter, although it seems likely that at least some of the occasional adult moths seen in the winter months may be immigrants from the warmer parts of the Continent. However, resident angle shades hatch from the eggs laid by the autumn brood and also feed up slowly through the winter on an enormous variety of plants and pupate at its end.

CHORUSING DARK BUSH-CRICKETS

On warm afternoons, and even more so after dark, from late July to early November, the rambler on the downs will very probably hear a chorus of short sharp chirps issuing forth from hedgebanks and woodland rides and borders, especially where there is an abundant cover of brambles and nettles. These high-pitched sounds, which, incidentally, become inaudible to most of us once we reach the age of forty or thereabouts, are produced by the males of the dark bush-cricket, a mainly dark-brown grasshopper-like insect up to 20 mm (1 in) long, with very long thread-like antennae. Only if we catch one and turn it upside down do we find the dark colour relieved by a bright-yellow or yellow-green belly. The females are larger and plumper than the males; they are easily recognized by their virtually wingless condition and possession of a flattened, upwards-curved ovipositor, up to 10 mm ($\frac{1}{2}$ in) long and shaped rather like a cutlass. The males are also flightless, the hindwings being absent and the forewings existing only in so far as they accommodate the areas modified for sound production. Like most bush-crickets, the males chirp by rubbing a toothed rib in the left forewing against the hind margin of the right forewing, where a roughly circular-shaped membrane (the 'mirror') amplifies the sound. While chirping ('stridulating'), their forewings are slightly raised as in most species of bush-crickets.

Although the males produce their instrumental chirps intermittently, they answer each other so that, when many are present, the result, as I have already indicated, is a chorus. This is especially noticeable where they are abundant. When two males meet they often respond aggressively to each other with a rapid series of longer, metallic chirps, and even scuffle briefly. Of course, the chief purpose of the chirping is to attract a receptive female. When her buff-coloured, cylindrical eggs are ready to be laid she deposits them in bark crevices or rotting wood. The young nymphs do not hatch from them until the next spring but one, and reach maturity in the following July or early August. In mild autumns some adult dark bush-crickets may not die off until late in November. Both sexes are agile and leap into cover if disturbed, although the females are easier to catch late in the season when they often move into long grass away from the protective cover of brambles and nettles. In sunny weather, both young nymphs and adults sun themselves on the upper surfaces of leaves.

Dark bush-crickets are omnivorous, feeding on the foliage of a wide range of plants and virtually any insects, spiders or other invertebrates that they can overcome. Incidentally, both adults and young (nymphs) can look remarkably

121

MUSHROOMS AND TOADSTOOLS

The shaggy parasol mushroom *Lepiota rhacodes* is, like the similar common parasol mushroom *L. procera*, an edible species growing in grassy places in woods and near their edges. It has shaggier scales on its dull brown cap, its whitish stem lacks the common parasol's brownish covering and its white flesh changes colour to reddish-brown when broken.

Red-staining inocybe, *Inocybe patouillardii* is another calcareous-loving toadstool of broad-leaved woods which prefers beeches. Deadly poisonous, it fruits from May to November, but is rather rare. The cap is white at first, but gradually changes through ivory-white to yellowish-brown, and turns blood-red where it becomes bruised or damaged. When young it is conical or bell-shaped, but flattens as it ages, and may split around the margins. The white gills gradually become olive-brown and turn reddish when rubbed. The white stem is flushed with red and striated with thread-like structures.

Bitter brittle-gill (geranium-scented russula) *Russula fellea*: is an inedible species with a very hot bitter taste, identified by its smell – like red geraniums. The cap, varying from straw to buff, has a smooth or slightly furrowed margin. The gills and stem are slightly paler than the cap. It is plentiful in beech woods from August to November.

Thought to be poisonous, the magpie ink cap *Coprinus picaceus*, with its pied patterned cap, becomes bell-shaped or conical as it matures. Eventually the cap flattens with age and curls up at the margins, while the gills gradually change from white to black, liquefy, and produce an inky fluid like other ink caps. It may be encountered growing singly in the leaf-litter, underneath beech or other broad-leaved trees, from September to December, but is not common.

The panther cap *Amanita pantherina* is a rather rare and very poisonous inhabitant of broad-leaved woods, found especially under beech trees from August to October. Its cap varies in colour from olive-umber through greyish olive to smoky brown, and is spotted with many small white warts which may feel sticky. Convex at first, the cap gradually flattens out and may become concave; its gills are white and not attached to the stem. The white stem has a bulbous base surrounded by several narrow, membrane-like rings and a white, rather narrow ring half-way up.

Plentiful in beech woods from August to November, the beech-wood sickener, *Russula mairei* is a poisonous relative of the bitter brittle-gill. The gills beneath the red or pink cap are at first greenish white, becoming cream-coloured later.

An edible species occurring quite commonly in broad-leaved woodlands on chalky soils is *Tricholoma argyraceum*, appearing especially in leaf litter under beeches from August to November. It has a convex cap, ranging in colour from whitish or pale grey through mouse-grey to pale brownish. Later on it flattens out and is marked with variable numbers of darkish scales. The gills are white or greyish, becoming yellowish later.

November 29th

Magpie ink cap 17th October
(Coprinus picaceus)

Tricholoma Argyraceum
11th November

21st October
Inocybe patouillardii

Panther Cap (Amanita pantherina)
29th October

Bitter Brittle-gill (Russula fellea)
23rd October

12th November
John Vaux

Beechwood Sickener
(Russula mairei)

like dark, long-legged spiders; this may afford them protection from some of their enemies. Apart from that, they are well camouflaged in the contrasting light and shade of dense vegetation. The species seems to have increased in numbers and spread on the North and South Downs, and elsewhere throughout south-east England in the course of this century, especially during the hot summers of the 1930s and 1940s, and the 1980s.

Autumnal blossoms

Fortunately for nectar-seeking insects, a great variety of summer wild flowerS continue to bloom deep into the autumn; some may still be flowering at the end of the year. On the downs these include marjoram, common and hoary ragwort, field and small scabious, burnet-saxifrage, bird's-foot trefoil, black knapweed, carline thistle, musk thistle, yellow toadflax, clary and chicory.

For some species autumn is the peak time of flowering. Among these may be numbered such downland specialities as autumn gentian, autumn lady's-tresses, deadly nightshade and hoary ragwort. Autumn gentian flowers from August to October, and is locally plentiful in many parts of both the North and the South

Downs. Localities for it include Box Hill, the Hog's Back and Selborne (North Downs) and Eastbourne, Beachy Head and Seaford (South Downs). As the late J. E. Lousley described in his book *Wild Flowers of Chalk and Limestone*, the bitter-tasting stems and leaves of autumn gentian are said to protect it against grazing animals, but are 'certainly of little value in the face of attacks from the hungry rabbits of the downs'. These nibble the young shoots down to the ground so that the plants are obliged to branch out from their bases and grow into bushy little tufts with numerous flowers. Lousley was writing in 1950 before the advent of myxomatosis decimated the rabbit populations, and allowed autumn gentian and chalk plants to grow normally in the short turf. In recent years, however, rabbits having recovered to a considerable extent, the gentians are once more subject to grazing pressure.

Looking towards Gilbert White's house – the Wakes – from Selborne Hanger.

In August and September, the latest of the British native orchids to flower, the often diminutive autumn lady's-tresses, will be found blossoming in short turf in some parts of the North and South Downs. Although the erect flowering stems are usually short (7–15 cm, $2\frac{3}{4}$–6 in) , rarely as much as 20 cm (8 in) (in longer grass), and thus inconspicuous, their elegant, spirally arranged small white tubular flowers attract the attention of the observant. He or she will then appreciate how the plant's name was acquired from its resemblance to the

125

long, curled and plaited tresses of past female hair-styles. The white blossoms, which have green centres, are fragrant with a scent likened by some to almond and by others to coconut! The rosette of oval, unstalked, bluish-green leaves, from the close vicinity of which the grey-green flowering stem arises, withers and dies long before the flowers open. However, close by new leaf rosettes are to be seen growing which live through the winter to produce new flowering stems late the following summer.

The flowers of autumn lady's-tresses are visited by bumble bees, although nobody seems to have checked this since Charles Darwin reported the fact. They are, in fact, as Darwin showed, splendidly adapted for cross-pollination

by insects such as bumble bees. The lowest flowers open before the upper ones and, when newly opened, cannot be pollinated by nectar-seeking bees until their pollinia (sticky pollen masses) are accidentally removed by the bee on the upper part of its tongue. When this happens, the stigma then becomes exposed and is pollinated by the next bee arriving with pollinia from the flowers of another plant. The bees also start their visits at the bottom of the flower spike, bringing pollinia to the exposed stigmas of these older flowers, and then working their way up to the younger flowers.

The strange-looking carline thistle is one of the most characteristic plants of chalk downland, and is to be found on more or less open grasslands throughout

This 'typical' chalk grassland at Fulking Escarpment is in fact a product of grazing: plants are all cropped short.

the North and South Downs. Growing up to 60 cm (2 ft) high, it is an erect, stiff and spiny plant with the prickly leaves so typical of thistles. In this case they are cottony underneath, especially the lower ones. The stems of the plant are also more or less cottony and often flushed with purple. The leaf-like outer bracts of the yellow-brown flower-heads, found singly or in clusters, are also cottony, and are spiny, while the straw yellow and narrow inner bracts have purple bases. These inner bracts, which spread out, looking like ray-florets (or petals), close up when the weather is wet, opening fully only in dry, sunny conditions. Because of this property of responding to humidity, country people sometimes collect them as a means of forecasting imminent changes in the weather. And despite their dry-looking, unappetizing appearance, butterflies quite often seek nectar from them. Carline thistle flowers late into the autumn, and even seems to do so throughout the winter. In fact, the plants die when wintery weather arrives, but still look much the same as they did when they were alive.

WILD FRUIT HARVEST

The colours of autumn vegetation are glorious, especially in wooded districts where the changing hues of the dying leaves of the trees grade from green through yellow and various shades of gold to rufous or tawny brown. Among the components of the colourful scenery are the various berries and fruits of trees, shrubs and certain plants: reds, blacks, purples and hues between. But they are not just beautiful; they are advertising their attractiveness to fruit-eating birds and other animals, inviting them to a feast with the end result that the plants' seeds will be distributed far and wide. On the chalk downs these advertisers include blackthorn, buckthorn, brambles, deadly nightshade, dog rose, dogwood, hawthorn, holly, juniper, rowan, spindle, traveller's joy, wayfaring tree, whitebeam and yew. As long as their fruits last there will be a procession of wild birds feasting on them, systematically stripping them away: blackbirds, mistle and song thrushes, fieldfares and redwings, ring ouzels, robins and bullfinches. The fieldfares and redwings will have arrived in October, from Scandinavia, to spend the winter in the milder conditions normally prevailing in southern England, while the ring ouzels will already have fattened up on the wild fruits, like haws and yew berries, at the end of September, and in early October, before passing on to winter quarters overseas. The other species mentioned remain with us throughout the year. All of them, apart from the bullfinch, swallow the berries whole, so that the seeds inside are passed unharmed through their digestive systems to germinate wherever they eventually excrete them. Thus the seeds are dispersed over a wide area to the advantage of the plants. And, of course, the advantage to the birds of this symbiotic relationship has been the nourishment the berries provide. This mutually beneficial relationship does not exist between all fruit-eating birds and fruit-bearing plants. Seed-eaters, such as the bullfinch and other finches, discard the 'flesh' of the fruits and eat the seeds.

As well as birds, many other animals feed on wild fruits in autumn. For instance, many insects will be seen imbibing the juices of over-ripe blackberries, such as bush-crickets, wasps, blow-flies, greenbottles and various other flies; but they play no part in the dispersal of the seeds. Among the mammals, small rodents, like dormice, bank and field voles, harvest mice and wood mice, consume their share of fruits and berries; and so do the larger grey and red squirrels. All help seed dispersal to some extent by burying surplus supplies. Badgers, foxes and deer also eat what comes their way.

Wood mice and other small mammals take advantage of the harvest of fruit and berries to fatten up before the winter.

Hazel nuts are, of course, from August to October a favourite food of squirrels, dormice, bank voles and wood mice (each of which has a distinctive method of reaching the kernel), as well as birds like nuthatches, and great spotted woodpeckers. Some apparently undamaged hazel nuts will, in fact, be found to have a small, neat round hole in them, the exit hole of the grub (larva) of a nut weevil. This had been feeding upon the kernel ever since it hatched from an egg laid by a female nut weevil when the nut first developed. She had inserted the egg after first boring a hole with her very long, curved snout (rostrum). When the hazel nut eventually fell to the ground, the grub ate its way out, burrowed into the soil and pupated. The adult beetles emerge in the spring. A similar species on oak lays its eggs singly in acorns.

The beech woods of the downs, especially in a favourable year, produce their nuts (beechmast) in abundance in September and October, an important source of food for all the mammals mentioned above and various birds (nuthatches,

129

blue and great tits, jays, etc.). In late autumn chaffinches and, sometimes, bramblings (another winter visitor from Scandinavia) flock to the beechmast littering the floor of the downland beech woods. Good beechmast years mean a better chance of survival through the winter for these birds.

Autumn fungi

A well-known feature of autumn is the abundance at this time of the aerial fruiting bodies of the macro fungi – the familiar mushrooms and toadstools. Although some species may fruit at other times of the year, or even througout the year, autumn is the peak time for the great majority. On the European mainland, but curiously much less so in Britain, very large numbers of people, in family parties, scour the woods and fields for the edible species.

On the subject of edibility or otherwise of fungi, it must, of course, be emphasized that nobody should venture to eat an unfamiliar species unless they are ABSOLUTELY SURE that they have correctly identified it, without any shadow of doubt, as an edible one. Although relatively few British species are poisonous, some, like the death cap and the panther cap, are extremely so, and even the consumption of a very small amount can prove fatal following exceedingly unpleasant and painful suffering. To avoid the danger of misidentification, fungi in the young button-like phase should not be eaten under any circumstances. Moreover, as some people may have allergic reactions to even edible species which most others can eat in perfect safety, it is advisable, when sampling a species not eaten before, to content oneself with only a very small amount. There are, by the way, no straightforward safe tests by which an edible species can be distinguished from a poisonous one, whatever some people may say (see pages 122–3).

Acrobatic long-tailed tits over Malling Down.

131

Gannet, puffin together with pomarine skua and great skua passing Beachy Head.

SEA-BIRD WATCHING FROM THE DOWNLAND CLIFFS

For many bird-watchers sea-bird watching is an intoxicating pursuit. It can be done at any time, but spring and autumn, when many sea-birds are migrating to or from their breeding sites, are the best. Autumn is, however, the period *par excellence* because their numbers are augmented by young birds.

Coastal promontories are the best places to look for sea-bird movements, as they pass close inshore. Chalk cliffs where the North and South Downs meet the sea provide excellent vantage points. Among these are North Foreland, near Broadstairs, Isle of Thanet; South Foreland and Shakespeare Cliff near Dover in Kent; and the Seven Sisters Cliffs and, above all, Beachy Head, near Eastbourne, in Sussex.

Beachy Head is the best place in East Sussex for watching sea-bird movements. From the top of the cliffs a commanding view can be obtained over the sea, while many of the birds come in quite close as they round the promontory. One can expect to see in autumn (August to October) movements of kittiwakes and other gulls, skuas, terns, petrels, shearwaters, gannets, auks, divers, eider ducks, and scoters. Take care not to fall off the cliffs!

A TIME OF HIGH ANIMAL MORTALITY

Although a time of great beauty in the downland landscapes and of abundant food, autumn is also a time of heavy mortality among wild animals, especially the young and inexperienced. Extensive ringing of nestling passerine birds has shown that a very high percentage fail to survive their first winter after leaving the nest: for example about 74 per cent of young robins and 87 per cent of young great tits. The annual death-rates of adults are lower, although still high; for instance 62 per cent of robins and about 48 per cent of great tits.

In all cases, however, those that survive their vulnerable first year of life have a good chance of living at least another year. The more experienced they become in the art of living and avoiding death from predators or other sources of danger, the greater their chances of fulfilling their average further life expectancy. Thus we can expect robins to live about 13 more months, blackbirds about 23 months, great tits 18 months and, in the case of the lapwing, a non-passerine, about two years.

These mortality rates are probably similar to those of mammals, the smaller species like mice, shrews and voles having a much lower life expectancy at birth than larger mammals such as badgers, foxes and deer. For instance, the potential expectation of life in the wild for a badger has been estimated at about 15 years, for a fox at 10 years, and for wood mice, shrews and voles at less than 2 years.

People often ask: 'If mortality is so high, why is it that we do not see many more dead birds and other animals lying about in the countryside?' The answer is that those which are killed by predators are normally eaten by them; often in cover where their remains are not so obvious when finally abandoned. Moreover, these remains, and those of the many other animals that die from natural causes, are consumed by carrion feeders, such as carrion crows, magpies, rats, carrion-feeding insects and certain fungi.

BURYING BEETLES

Conspicuous among the carrion-feeding insects are the burying or sexton beetles. These rather large beetles are attracted to the corpses of small animals, such as birds, voles and mice, and bury them by scraping away the soil underneath so that they are gradually lowered into the ground. Several burying beetles are usually attracted to the same corpse and work together in pairs until nothing is to be seen of it, apart from a low mound of soil. This done, each female usually drives away the male, then makes a ball of chewed meat and deposits it in a chamber beneath the corpse. Next, she constructs a short shaft leading out of it in which she lays her eggs. When they hatch, the young larvae make their way to the chamber where the female is guarding the meat ball. She then feeds them with droplets of brown fluid – regurgitated carrion – until they are big enough to eat the ball by themselves. When all of it has been consumed, they move on to the rest of the carcass and complete their development. Like

AUTUMN DIARY

Also known as felwort, the reddish-purple flowers of the autumn gentian are very sensitive to temperature, opening and closing rapidly when the sun comes out or disappears behind thick cloud. More will be found about it on pages 124–5.

These redstarts on the South Downs on 19 September 1990 were busy feeding up on elderberries and insects before departing on their long, energy-sapping migration to the southern edge of the Sahara. It is vital that they build up their fat reserves before quitting the south coast. The male hovering was fly-catching, a common habit of redstarts and warblers as well as pied and spotted flycatchers.

The lesser whitethroat is another warbler which is fond of eating berries and fruit in late summer and autumn in addition to its main diet of insects. Lesser whitethroats, like this one portrayed on Lychpole Hill in late September 1990, also congregate in scrub along the South Downs and feed voraciously before setting off on their nocturnal sea crossing – in this case bound for winter quarters in north-east Africa, an unusual destination for British summer residents.

Another insectivorous warbler that consumes a lot of fruit in late summer and autumn, like the one in the illustration, feasting on blackberries, is the blackcap. Most breeding here in the summer migrate to Spain and north Africa for the winter.

The silver y moths pictured by John Davis were among hundreds he saw on Barlavington Down, West Sussex, on 31 August 1990. They may have been a swarm of home-bred moths which were in a migratory phase and preparing to attempt a southwards migration to southern Europe or even north Africa. However, they might also have arrived over the sea from the south, as they often do in late summer and September.

The habit of squirrels of hoarding surplus acorns and hazelnuts in autumn, particularly in October, by burying them is well known and, since they subsequently fail to relocate many of these in the winter, they are important agents in the plants' dispersal and successful germination. Jays, too, share this habit of burying acorns (as to some extent do magpies and other crows) and, because of the large scale on which they do so, they play a very important part in the natural regeneration of oak woods. Those that they and the grey squirrels rediscover during later food shortages help them to get through the winter.

Autumn is the rutting (mating) time for the fallow deer pictured here, as well as for the red deer, the fallow deer bucks beginning when the red deer stags have passed their peak period. Fierce as such contests look, they rarely end in serious injury; the one that feels he has lost quickly retreats to fight another day.

17th September
most over. some in bud.
Autumn Gentian

Hackpole Hill
22nd Sept.
lesser Whitethroat in scrub.

19th September

Several Redstarts

27th September

Hundreds of Silver Y's
Barbardington Down 31st August

23rd October

23rd October

John Davis

A fallow buck bellowing his challenge to his rivals after having marked out his territory.

the adults, they also attack and eat the many other species of carrion beetles, and other scavenging insects and their larvae which are attracted to the site, and which they are able to overcome. In a week or so the larvae are fully grown, whereupon they burrow deeper into the soil and pupate. The adults meanwhile, when not otherwise engaged with a corpse, hide in shallow burrows, in which they also spend the winter.

There are six species of burying beetles of the genus *Nicrophorus* in Britain. Of these, one species *N. humator* is entirely black and can be easily distinguished from the other five, all of which are black with conspicuous orange-red markings on their wing-cases. However, the all-black *humator* could be confused with a similar-looking carrion beetle of the related genus *Necrodes*, but can be identified by its antennae which end in distinct orange clubs. This species, *N. littoralis*, as its scientific name implies, is found mainly along or near the coast. Here it feeds and lays its eggs upon, but does not bury, large carcasses. In such situations it occurs where both the North and South Downs reach the coast. The orange-red and black-patterned species are not easy to tell apart from each other, except for *Nicrophorus vespilloides*, which has black clubs at the tips of its black antennae, whereas the other species have orange clubs to theirs. All the British species of *Nicrophorus* fly well and are to be found on both the North and South Downs.

THE DEER RUT

Autumn is, of course, the rutting time for our native red deer and the fallow deer which has been established here since time immemorial. The bellowing roar of a rutting red deer stag must be familiar to most people – from radio and television programmes if they have not heard it in the wild. It begins in late September, reaches a peak in the first half of October and dies down thereafter. Red deer are most likely to be seen in downland parks, except in the west of the area covered by the North and South Downs, where some roam wild.

Fallow deer do not begin to rut until well into October, and finish around the middle of November. Having marked his mating territory by fraying young trees with his antlers and urinating beneath them, each buck challenges his rivals with a rhythmic belching, grunting bark. As with all deer, the resultant battles, consisting of head-butting and antler wrestling, rarely end in serious injury to the combatants. The victorious buck rounds up his harem of does and mates with them, leaving his defeated rivals to fight each other on their own mating territories, or 'rutting stands', for the remaining ones. The younger bucks can be recognized by the traces of velvet remaining on their antlers. Following the end of the rut, separate herds of bucks and does form and stay together until late spring, after which the fawns are born. Fallow deer are often kept in parks, but are also to be seen wild in Challock Forest, Kent, on the North Downs and in Charlton and Slindon Forests, and in the woods of Kingley Vale on the South Downs in Sussex.

Roe deer bucks, having already rutted in August, lose their antlers in November or early December, and are therefore the only species in velvet during the winter. Older bucks, which have already lost their antlers, may be challenged at this time by younger ones still in possession of theirs, and feeling sexually active. When rutting in August, the bucks become restless and bark and rasp a good deal. When a doe enters a rutting area within the buck's territory, he sniffs and then pursues her round and round in circles before mating. This behaviour is at least one of the causes of the circular tracks around a tree or bush known as 'roe-rings'. Intruding rival bucks are chased off, sometimes after a fight that may occasionally result in serious injury. After mating, the implantation of the fertilized egg is delayed in the doe until December, with the fawns, known as kids in the roe deer, being born between April and July. Twins and even triplets are not uncommon. Unlike other deer, roe deer do not form harems, although the bucks mate with more than one doe. At present, roe deer are only found in good numbers in the downland woods in the west of the area of the North and South Downs, but are, nevertheless, increasing and spreading eastwards.

WINTER

uperficially, the open downlands can seem relatively empty of life on a cold winter's day, but there is still plenty of interest if you know where to look for it. Of course, the great majority of plants do not flower at this season, and will have withdrawn their life force to their rootstock or basal leaves in the case of perennials and biennials, while the seeds of annuals and first year biennials will be germinating or lying dormant until spring. Many animals, mainly invertebrates like butterflies, hibernate through the winter in the stage of their life cycle which they have reached; others, such as some birds, will have migrated to warmer climes.

On the other hand, resident birds stay in Britain and are joined by a host of others escaping less mild winter climates, while many other animals, including the majority of species of mammals and many invertebrates, remain active. Moreover, some insects, such as certain moths, actually time their appearance as perfect adult insects to coincide with the months of winter. All animals that remain active through the cold, inhospitable winter months have evolved adaptations which enable them to cope with harsh conditions and food shortages. Some mammals, for example, which do not hibernate, develop thicker coats of insulating fur and extra layers of fat, and store hoards of foods when they are plentiful in the autumn, drawing on them when they need to do so. Birds also put on more fat in autumn to tide them over cold periods of food shortage and some, such as jays, nuthatches and tits, store food like squirrels.

Like foxes, shrews, squirrels and other mammals, in the autumn deer begin growing a thicker and duller winter coat. The spotting on fallow deer either fades considerably or disappears altogether. The smallest deer now living wild in England is the muntjac, its ancestors having originally escaped from stock introduced into Woburn Park, Bedfordshire, around 1900 by the then Duke of Bedford. It has steadily been spreading throughout the woodlands of central England since about 1950 and is gradually penetrating those of the extreme south-east. It has already appeared in some of the woods along the western half of the North Downs, including the Hog's Back and Dorking areas of Surrey, and also along the much more wooded western part of the South Downs. Muntjac are very secretive, choosing woods with dense secondary vegetation, and with their small size are therefore not easily seen, except with a lot of time

Roe hinds in December, near Kingley Vale: they separate from the males once the rutting season is over. As can be seen, the traveller's joy in the background well deserves its country name of old man's beard.

139

and patience. However, at times they betray their presence by continuous barking with roughly five-second intervals between each bark (they are called barking deer in their native Asia), and so give you a rough indication of where you should conceal yourself and watch. Unlike other species of deer in Britain, they rut and breed at almost any time. The muntjac's large eyes and acute sense of smell fits it well for a nocturnal life, but it is also active by day, especially in the hour or so before dusk. It browses on grass, brambles, ivy and very young trees, and eats some fruits and nuts as well. Although capable of living up to fourteen years, few muntjacs achieve this in the wild. Mortality is at its heaviest in winter, when most road casualties, the biggest known cause of death, occur. Many others are shot, while foxes, dogs and cats account for many fawns.

OTHER MAMMALS IN WINTER

Only a relatively few British mammals – all species of bats, hedgehog and dormice – undergo true hibernation. From the middle of December to the middle of February, badgers are much less active and spend a lot of their time sleeping in their underground setts, drawing to a large extent on the fat reserves built up in autumn; but they do not actually hibernate. Badger cubs may actually be born as early as the middle of January. Grey squirrels, too, may spend more time sleeping in their thick winter nests than usual, living off their fat reserves, especially in very bad weather; but they are, in fact, capable of

The roe buck loses his antlers soon after the rutting season is over.

going only a few days without food. They feed actively in the daylight hours of winter, when weather conditions allow, on almost anything edible they can find: this includes food on bird tables, seeds and berries, fungi, bulbs and roots, insects and their larvae, and, most of all, acorns, beechmast and other nuts still lying where they have fallen in the autumn. When these become scarce they search for those acorns and nuts they buried in the autumn, using scent to locate them; however, their memory of precisely where to look does not seem to be good and they miss many, thus unintentionally aiding the dispersal of the trees.

For protection from the cold, when not sheltering in their strongly constructed winter dreys, grey squirrels rely on the dense coat of silvery grey fur, tinged with yellowish brown on the head and back, which develops over six weeks in the autumn, beginning from the rump forwards. Already in mid-winter the churring males may begin their courtship chases of the females, with the result that the earliest of the spring litters of usually three young may be born in the winter drey as early as late December or early January; however, most will be born between then and April. Summer litters are born in the period May to July. Many young squirrels perish during the rigours of their first winter, but the survivors, barring accidents, are capable of living for up to ten years. Grey squirrels are common in most of the woods of the North and South Downs, and have successfully penetrated into the gardens and parks of most town and city suburbs.

Mice, shrews and voles are other mammals which exchange their thinner and brighter summer coat for a thicker, duller one in winter. None of them hibernate; instead they keep up their ceaseless, restless and urgent search for food throughout the winter months, tunnelling through the grass beneath any snowfall, however heavy. Even so, in times of food shortage wood mice (long-tailed field mouse) may become torpid for a spell, rather as if hibernating, thereby saving energy until things improve. In milder winter weather they and yellow-necked mice climb into bushes and trees in search of hawthorn berries and similar fruits and seeds, sometimes storing them in an old bird's nest and using it as a feeding place. Harvest mice construct neatly woven winter nests of grass low down or on the ground in a grass tussock or beneath a hedge, whereas their summer nests are built well above ground, woven among the stalks of tall plants, long grass, reeds or growing corn. During the winter they spend most of their time searching for seeds, berries and non-hibernating insects on or near the ground, where they make use of the runway systems of other small rodents.

Bank voles, short-tailed field voles and shrews shelter in underground tunnels. The last-named have to maintain their ceaseless, almost frenzied search for worms and other soil invertebrates, otherwise they will die of starvation if they fail to find sufficient food within a few hours. Voles, on the other hand, often store berries, nuts, seeds and other vegetable food in an underground chamber and consume it at leisure. They are active by day and night like shrews, taking frequent short rests and naps in the same way. As their large round ears and eyes indicate, wood and yellow-necked mice are nocturnal, while the small-eared harvest mouse is active in the daytime as well as at night.

WINTER DIARY

Beacon Hill, towering 793 feet (242 metres) above the small villages of Elsted and East Harting, not far to the south-east of Petersfield, forms the centrepiece of the illustrations on the opposite page. In suitable habitats on the lower slopes of its massive bulk, beneath the encircling earthworks of the ancient hill fort, it is possible to see all the wildlife portrayed in the surrounding studies. The South Downs Way skirts it to the east and south.

Mid-winter is mating time for the fox, Britain's largest land mammal carnivore; it is therefore a time of great activity for both sexes. Courtship begins towards the end of the year and continues into February. After dark they may be heard uttering their distinctive high-pitched barks, while now and again the vixens may call to the dog-foxes with shrill, unearthly screams. Various other barks and cries are also to be heard. The pairs keep company for nearly a month, hunting together, and during this period the dog follows the vixen for long periods with his tail outstretched and mates with her on several occasions, sometimes for up to half an hour at a time.

The tiny goldcrest and firecrest, the smallest insectivorous birds in Britain, are regarded as warblers nowadays and certainly have much in common with them, but in some respects they are tit-like and, outside the breeding season, may often be seen accompanying roving bands of those very active birds. They are restless, constantly flitting from twig to twig in thick cover, snatching a small spider here or an insect there, and often hovering under a branch to look for invertebrates beneath it.

The goldcrest is much the commoner of the two, both being found in woods, especially coniferous ones. Firecrests are mainly passage migrants, passing through southern England, like the one pictured here in the Arun Valley, in autumn, winter and early spring. Since the 1960s, however, firecrests have been breeding in very small numbers. They are easily overlooked and it is probable that a very few pairs nest in suitable woods on the North and South Downs. As the illustrations show clearly, the firecrest's pronounced black and white eye stripes and bronze neck patches separate it from the duller goldcrest.

In the winter months quite large parties of the engaging little long-tailed tits which, were it not for their very long tails, are hardly bigger than goldcrests, will be encountered in woods and hedgerows searching, like that species, for small invertebrates. Their constant purring and shrill 'zee-zee-zee' contact calls often attract attention before they come into view. They are a fairly common breeding bird of woodland and scrub on both the North and South Downs.

The bright red 'hairy' growths of the robin's pincushions among the hips of the dog rose above the long-tailed tits, on the left-hand side of the plate, are galls caused by small black and red gall wasps *Diplolepis rosae*: their fascinating life cycle is related on page 161.

Mice, shrews and voles have many enemies and suffer heavy annual mortality, relatively few surviving their first winter, and even fewer surviving for as much as a year or more. However, their losses are made good by their high rate of breeding and, in some years, plagues of field voles may occur. Many mice and voles fall prey to owls, stoats, weasels, foxes and cats, and the diurnally active harvest mice and voles to kestrels and other raptors, crows and herons. Shrews are usually shunned by many predators, such as foxes, cats and mustelids (weasels, etc.), because of the repellant, strong-smelling and foul-tasting glands in their skin; owls, however, are not put off and eat great numbers.

Wood mice are not necessarily restricted to woodland and, like yellow-necked mice, harvest mice, bank voles, common, pygmy and water shrews, will be found living in scrub, hedgerows and field margins as well. Although often living along streams and around ponds, in which they will hunt small aquatic animals, water shrews are not confined to watery habitats and can also be found on, for example, chalk downland. As its name implies, the field vole prefers open grassland, particularly where it is rough and tussocky; some, however, live amongst scrub or in open woodland and young plantations where there is plenty of grass, their staple food. Common, pygmy and water shrews, harvest mice and wood mice, bank voles and field voles are common (perhaps rather less so in the case of the harvest mouse in some districts) throughout the area covered by this book. The yellow-necked mouse is also well distributed throughout the area, but is much less common than the wood mouse. Incidentally, the former is more likely to enter houses and other buildings in search of stored food and winter shelter than the latter.

THE HIBERNATORS

As already mentioned, relatively few British mammals undergo true hibernation; only the bats, the dormice and the hedgehog. During this prolonged winter sleep, the animal's metabolism slows right down and, in the case of mammals, its body temperature drops to about that of its surroundings. The body temperature of bats drops from a normal 36°C to 8°C, and the breathing rate to ten times slower than normal, frequently ceasing altogether for longish periods. Despite their apparent unconsciousness in this torpid state bats are easily disturbed and aroused by sudden noise or a rise in temperature. Such arousal causes their heartbeat and breathing rate to quicken until they begin to shiver, a state which is believed to speed up the return to normal body temperature. It takes at least a quarter of an hour before they are warm enough to fly. So a rise in temperature in a mild winter can cause bats to wake up and even venture out to feed by day as well as night, although they will find relatively few active, flying insects on which to prey.

This lack of flying insects in winter is the reason that the insectivorous bats hibernate in temperate climates. Like other mammals and birds, they build up the fat reserves in their bodies when food is abundant in the late summer and autumn, and depend upon it during the winter months. Hibernation is a strategy that ensures that these fat reserves last as long as possible by using only the bare minimum of energy. Bats employ it even in the summer by becoming torpid in their roosts during prolonged inclement spells of bad weather which cause moths and other crepuscular or night-flying insects to become torpid as well. Although, in winter, bats do need to wake up from hibernation from time to time, when weather conditions allow, to excrete and drink, and, if possible, feed, it should not happen too often, otherwise the energy-saving strategy is defeated and they might become seriously weakened.

Of the fifteeen species of bats known to be resident in Britain, ten occur within the area of the North and South Downs. Eight of them – the whiskered, Natterer's, Daubenton's, serotine, noctule, pipistrelle, barbastelle and common long-eared bats – are well distributed throughout the North and South Downs and may be common locally, except for the barbastelle which is very rare. Leisler's bat, which looks very like a small noctule bat, is also rare and appears to be confined to the western sector of the North Downs. So far, the uncommon Brandt's bat is known only from the North Downs, although it may yet be discovered in the wooded areas of the South Downs, at it is known to occur over a wide area of England and Wales.

Most British bats inhabit wooded districts, often roosting in holes in trees, especially hollow ones, as well as in caves and buildings; although some, like the serotine, pipistrelle and whiskered, may live happily enough in more open habitats, such as farmland and urban districts. Daubenton's bat, also known as the water bat, because of its fondness for hunting low over ponds and lakes in open, wooded areas for the insects associated with watery places, is only likely to be seen where dew ponds occur on the downs or along the river valleys that cut through the chalk. Intensive forestry and agriculture, with their great use of pesticides, plus the over-zealous tidying up of the countryside through the removal of old, decaying and hollow trees is adversely affecting bats by depleting their insect food supply and the loss of roosting and hibernation sites. This is unfortunate as bats, which in Britain are all protected species, help to control the numbers of many nocturnal insects, some of which are injurious to agriculture, in an environmentally friendly way.

For most people the mammal that most readily comes to mind as a hibernator, thanks to Lewis Carroll's *Alice in Wonderland*, is the common dormouse. Nowadays, it is regarded as an uncommon species, but is probably much overlooked in these times of mechanical hedge-cutting and trimming. Indeed, many may perish through the use of machines for these tasks, they and their summer nests being unfeelingly hacked to pieces, since tall and thick, species-rich hedgerows are one of their favourite habitats. They also inhabit dense scrub, coppiced woodland and broad-leaved woods with plenty of tall undergrowth, feeding after dark on acorns, beechmast, hazel, sweet chestnut and other nuts, pollen, berries, fruit and various insects. Hazel nuts eaten by dormice can be recognized by the way in which they have smooth, round holes gnawed in them without the obvious teeth marks left by bank voles and wood

mice. Agile climbers, dormice construct their summer nests well above ground in a bush, preferably one protected with thorns, and use grass, thin strips of bark (especially honeysuckle), dead leaves and moss to weave the ball-shaped structure. In the autumn they build their individual winter nests on, just above or just below the ground surface, often amongst tree roots, and hibernate within from about October to April. They fall asleep for the winter when the outside temperature drops continuously below 15°C, but awake occasionally during mild spells of weather and become active. Sometimes, common dormice occupy bird nest-boxes, even when they are erected on tree trunks as much as three metres or so (10 ft) above ground. The area which includes the North and South Downs appears to have the highest density of common dormice in Britain and they are probably fairly plentiful in most wooded parts of these downs.

Most people know that hedgehogs hibernate, and many garden owners have found them doing so in their winter nests of dead leaves and grass hidden under or behind a garden shed, in a compost heap or beneath a hedge. Sometimes, they may be unfortunate enough to choose to burrow into an unlit bonfire, especially one being prepared in October for Guy Fawkes night celebrations – a check should be made before lighting, to prevent them perishing. A large number of hedgehogs, in any case, die from starvation and other natural causes during hibernation, particularly young animals doing so for the first time. Others, of course, especially again young ones, may be found by predators such as badgers, foxes or dogs, which find a way of killing them even though they are rolled up in a protective ball with all their formidable spines pointing outwards. October is the month in which adult hedgehogs start to hibernate, though younger ones may not do so for another month or more. They often

Fields of autumn-planted crops provide pickings for birds during the winter, such as grey partridges, yellowhammers, linnets, lapwings and skylarks.

147

build more than one winter nest, waking in mild spells and moving their hibernating quarters. As with bats and dormice, they accumulate large deposits of fat to see them through the period of hibernation, during which their metabolism similarly slows right down, their heart rate slowing from 190 beats per minute to 20, and their respiration to an irregular 10 or so breaths a minute.

Usually about April, hedgehogs emerge from hibernation and resume the serious business of eating a wide variety of invertebrate animals, from caterpillars and large beetles to earthworms, slugs, spiders and woodlice. They will also eat fruit, berries, carrion and, if they find them, birds' eggs and their nestlings. Mating takes place soon after hibernation, following a simple courtship in which the male circles the female, snorting all the while. Hedgehogs are, of course, mainly nocturnal, but can sometimes be met with during the daytime. Sadly, most of those seen in the daytime are road casualties, mortality from this cause being unnecessarily heavy. Drivers could avoid at least some of them if they drove more slowly and with greater attention to the road ahead. Despite such needless losses, hedgehogs are still common and are found almost everywhere on the North and South Downs and the surrounding areas, particularly where there is sufficient cover in the form of long grass, scrub, hedgerows and broad-leaved woodland.

DOWNLAND WOODS IN WINTER

In winter the woodlands on the downs, especially the beech woods, are silent places – except when one happens to chance upon a mixed flock of tits and nuthatches; or perhaps disturbs a mixed flock of chaffinches and bramblings from the fallen beechmast; or sends a cock pheasant rocketing off with loud, echoing alarm calls, stimulating a jay or two into harsh, rasping cries of alarm. One of the bird calls to be frequently heard in the woods on the North and South Downs, and whose plaintiveness seems to be the epitome of a wood in winter, is the quiet piping of the bullfinch. The pairs are often well hidden in a thicket and all one may glimpse of them as they fly away is the conspicuous and distinctive white rump possessed by both sexes. Move quietly or wait patiently, so that they are not disturbed, and they will probably come into view: the adult males are incredibly handsome in their livery of brick-red underparts, blue-grey back, white rump and lower belly, jet-black head cap, tail and wings, and white wing-bar. Seen against snow on a sunny day, the male makes a beautiful picture. The females and first-winter males are similar, but much duller, with a brownish tinge. A male and female will normally be encountered together, as they pair for life. Sometimes in the winter the pairs and immature birds combine to form small parties, and occasionally flocks of up to 50 or so birds are reported. At this time of the year they feed mainly on seeds, berries and any insects, spiders or other invertebrates they come across. Throughout the North and South Downs bullfinches are common breeding birds where sufficient cover exists, not only in woodland, and often nest in orchards and gardens, even in suburbia. In winter they will come into gardens to feed, including small ones where they do not breed, and may visit bird tables.

Shy though the bullfinch tends to be, the larger hawfinch is even shyer and more secretive in its behaviour. The south-east of England is one of its strongholds in Britain and it breeds in small numbers in mature broad-leaved and mixed woodlands, and in adjacent orchards and large, wooded gardens over most of the North and South Downs, especially the former. The hawfinch is, however, an elusive bird and easily overlooked, so it may be a commoner

The nuthatch's preferred habitat is old deciduous woods, where it can nest in holes in trees.

species than a look through county bird reports suggests, although its breeding populations seem subject to marked fluctuations. It is most easily located when its loud and sharp, great spotted woodpecker-like 'ptik' contact call is heard; and, when seen, its large size for a finch and top heavy appearance due to its massive bill, thick neck and short tail is distinctive, even in silhouette. Hawfinches often flock during the winter when they may be met with on the woodland floor, feeding on beechmast or, later in the winter, on hornbeam seeds. On the North Downs in Surrey, they have been observed following thrushes eating yew berries and eating the seeds which the thrushes have discarded. They are also fond of hawthorn berries, sloes (blackthorn fruits), maple seeds and, in summer, cherries (wild cherry trees are often a feature of the beech woods). In summer they also eat insects and, in spring, flower and leaf buds. Towards spring the individuals become more aggressive towards each other within the flocks, which then eventually break up. The males then establish their territories and pursue prospective mates through the tree tops, also indulging in courtship display flights.

A notable place where hawfinches can be found is Kingley Vale National Nature Reserve, on the West Sussex downs near Chichester, which has perhaps the finest natural yew forest in Europe. Some of the largest trees here are said to be up to 500 years old. Those on the chalk slopes are younger, up to 200 years or so, and are intermingled here and there with ash. Away from the yew forest, with its dense, dark-green canopy, ash and oak become dominant, but holly and such typical chalk-loving trees and shrubs as buckthorn, dogwood, maple

Old yew tree at Kingley Vale.

and spindle grow among them as secondary cover, something almost entirely missing in the yew woods. There are also areas of open downland and chalk heath at Kingley Vale. Buzzards and woodcock are among the rarer birds occurring in this reserve in winter.

Other birds of the downland woods in winter, besides parties and flocks of finches, include congregations of foraging tits (blue, coal, great, marsh and long-tailed) working their way through the trees, accompanied by goldcrests, nuthatches, tree creepers and the occasional great spotted and lesser spotted woodpecker. Sometimes they are alarmed by a marauding sparrow hawk taking one of their number in a surprise attack. Flocks of wood pigeons join the chaffinches and bramblings to feed on the beechmast, while at night tawny owls and long-eared owls hunt the wood mice and other small mammals that come out to feed. At dusk both species, especially the long-eared, also take small birds as they go to roost. Both breed at Kingley Vale.

During the daytime the whereabouts of a roosting owl may be disclosed by its discovery by tits, blackbirds, chaffinches, jays and other birds which utter a noisy chorus of alarm calls. Otherwise, a circle of white excreta and pellets around a tree may indicate an occupied roost. Several long-eared owls, whose numbers are augmented in the autumn by continental immigrants, may occupy a single roost; up to a dozen being recorded on occasions. Nevertheless, long-eared owls are easily and often overlooked. Records suggest that they are thinly, but well distributed, through the woods, plantations and copses, especially coniferous ones, of the North and South Downs, notably in Kent. Before the winter ends, in February, the resident male long-eared owls occupy their breeding territories and court the females with wing-clapping and slow display-flights. Their low quavering, but far-carrying, long drawn-out moaning hoot will be heard at this time, and for a month or so more. The female usually lays her three to six white eggs in the disused nest of a crow, magpie, heron, grey squirrel, or some other species. Tawny owls begin nesting a little later, in March, more often in a hole in a tree than an old nest.

WINTERING BIRDS AND THEIR BEHAVIOUR

Many species of birds join together and feed in flocks during the autumn and winter. The chief advantage of such flocking behaviour is that, by day or night, a number of birds feeding together are more likely to notice the approach of a predator, such as a sparrow hawk, than a solitary bird and can thus warn each other. This is particularly important in winter when there is relatively less cover after deciduous foliage has fallen. An additional advantage is that, since there are a number of 'sentries' at any given time, the individual is able to spend less time on the alert and more time in feeding and resting – another important point in winter when it is even more necessary to eat as much as possible and conserve energy. Different species, as we have seen, regularly flock together and it is an interesting fact that some have evolved special predator alarm calls or even mutually similar ones (for example, great tits and chaffinches) to which the species involved all react.

In the course of a winter walk over the downs you are bound to see, at the very least, some flocks of birds feeding busily. Apart from the chaffinches, bramblings and wood pigeons in the beech and oak woods, the arable fields will contain mixed or pure flocks of various species of finches, buntings and sparrows, starlings, skylarks, meadow pipits, pied wagtails, fieldfares, red-wings, black-headed and common gulls, partridges, lapwings, golden plover, jackdaws and rooks, stock doves and yet more wood pigeons. Some of these species – starlings, skylarks, linnets, greenfinches, meadow pipits, fieldfares, redwings and jackdaws – will also be found searching for sustenance in the downland turf with parties of mistle thrushes, magpies, pheasants and loose assemblies of blackbirds, song thrushes and other species.

Towards dusk all these flocking species will seek communal roosts, and their behaviour at this time is well worth watching. The rooks and jackdaws fly off to

a favoured wood in flocks of a hundred or so, as well as in long, straggling lines. There they may be joined by carrion crows and magpies which often like to share their roost. Some of these corvid roosts are very large. Towards sunrise the birds stir and, once some have made the first move, then they all beat their way, again in long, straggling flocks and groups to resume feeding in the fields.

Wood pigeons and stock doves also roost communally in the woods, often in huge numbers, such as the 3000 or so that use Cissbury Ring. Pheasants are very noisy at dusk before settling down in their roosts in tall scrub or woodland. Lapwings and golden plover continue to feed in the fields at night, especially by moonlight, resting at intervals, as they do during the day; they may be heard calling quite frequently through the hours of darkness. The black-headed and other gulls leave the downland fields as dusk descends and fly to roost either along the river estuaries or on the still waters of large inland reservoirs, such as Bewl Water in the Weald, not far from Tunbridge Wells. In late autumn the resident British population of starlings is reinforced by an influx of immigrants

Downland woods looking east from Bignor Hill to West Burton Hill. Even in the milder southern part of the British Isles, this is a hard time for animals.

from the Continent. These spend the nights in often huge roosts in the country-side in contrast to the great urban roosts of those British starlings which live within a ten mile or so radius of a town or city. Notable starling winter roosts on the North and South Downs often hold between 5000 and 20,000 birds.

Little seems to be known about the roosting behaviour of winter flocks of skylarks, but they presumably sleep close together in whatever cover they can find. Meadow pipit flocks either roost in rough grassy places near their feeding areas or fly to nearby reed-beds, sometimes in company with pied wagtails. As well as flying to the reed-beds in the river valleys below the downs, pied wagtails also roost on buildings or in trees growing along urban streets, such as the 182 counted roosting outside a bookshop in Eastbourne in March 1989. The sometimes huge flocks of fieldfares and redwings which, following their arrival from Scandinavia, frequent the downs, feeding in both arable fields and on the crops of haws and other berries, usually roost in the hedgerows as long as they are thick and high enough. As they settle down for the night, redwings often indulge in a good deal of subsong. Finch and bunting flocks also roost in

hedgerows or other thick cover, such as reeds or tall, coarse vegetation; sometimes more than one species roosts together.

Redwings and fieldfares on Lullington Heath, near Windover Hill. Members of the thrush family, they feed in open fields and hedgerows in flocks.

WINTER MOTHS

Mid-winter seems an unlikely time for moths to choose to emerge from their pupae. Naturally, we associate them with warm summer nights; yet the observant motorist driving along woodland roads on mild winter nights will have noticed what look like pale-looking moths fluttering in his or her headlights across the road ahead. They are indeed moths: several species are abroad at this apparently unpropitious time, some of them appearing at no other season of the year. However, they only do so in mild weather. Some are named after their chief period of emergence: the November moth, the December moth, the early moth, the March moth and the delightfully named spring usher. All of these are common on the North and South Downs.

155

The most abundant of all species is the aptly named winter moth, a Geometer, and something of a pest as its thin green caterpillars are one of the chief defoliators of broad-leaved and orchard trees. Appearing as early as October, the adult moths can be found throughout the winter months in wooded districts as late as February. The male has fully developed greyish-brown wings, crossed by darker lines and bands, but the female, like some other autumn, winter and very early spring species, is virtually wingless and quite unable to fly. The males have to seek the females on the tree-trunks on to which they have climbed on emerging from their pupae. After mating, the female lays clusters of greenish-white eggs, which later turn orange, in crevices in the bark or on unopened buds on the twigs. Early in April the young looper caterpillars of the winter moth hatch and feed on the opening buds, blossom and foliage of the tree. At times they may be present in such large numbers that whole trees may be partly or even completely defoliated by them. Not only are apple and other fruit trees subject to the ravages of these caterpillars, but so are oaks and many other species of shrubs and trees. When full grown in late May or in June, the caterpillars descend to the ground and pupate in the soil. The larger, paler and glossier northern winter moth is also common on the North and South Downs and has a similar life history to the winter moth, except that the females have slightly larger vestigial wings.

The November moth and the mottled umber are two other very common Geometer moths whose larvae can cause great damage in spring to orchards as well as to many of our native broad-leaved trees. The November moth is rather similar to the winter moth, except that it is larger and fully winged in both sexes. It flies in October and November from dusk onwards, often coming to lighted windows. During the day November moths rest, well camouflaged, on tree-trunks, fences and twigs. They are easily disturbed from these resting places, however, and may sometimes be encountered fluttering through the woods at any hour of the day. Although very variable, the handsomely dark-banded, light brown wings of the male mottled umber are distinctive enough to distinguish it from the much paler scarce umber, the only similar species on the wing between October and January. The flight of the latter, however, is normally over by December. The females of both species are flightless, those of the mottled umber being completely wingless and spider-like; they have to use their leg power to climb the trees and lay their egg batches in the bark crevices, where they remain until they hatch the following spring. Although the scarce umber is, in spite of its name, fairly common in English and Welsh woodlands, including those of the North and South Downs, it is not common enough to be considered a pest of the many deciduous trees upon which, like the others, its caterpillars feed during the spring. As with the November moth, the mottled and scarce umber females may be found in the daylight hours as well as after dark sitting on tree-trunks and fences, while the males perch on the twigs of trees and bushes; on mild nights they can be discovered quite easily by the light of a torch, to which they seem to be drawn. The males are also readily attracted to artificial light in buildings.

As its name indicates, early in the year, in January and February, providing the weather is mild, the early moth makes its appearance. Scores of the males and the almost wingless females of this drab and undistinguished, brownish little moth can be observed by torchlight, sitting on the stems and at the ends of the twigs of its larval foodplants, blackthorn and hawthorn, in hedgerows and around the borders of woods throughout the downs. The males fly at dusk and are often to be seen spotlighted in the headlights of a car as they flit along the hedgerows or cross the road. The females lay their eggs more or less where they have chosen to sit, the caterpillars hatching after the leaves have opened.

A lot of these moths of winter fall prey to the eager bands of foraging tits, tree creepers and other birds whose sharp eyes and probing beaks discover them in their daytime resting places, in spite of their usually effective camouflage, just as they find their caterpillars in the spring. Nevertheless, enough survive to maintain healthy populations. The adult moths' main nocturnal predators seem to be shrews, wood mice, owls and perhaps, when the weather is warm enough to tempt them temporarily out of hibernation, bats.

The woodcock is a solitary bird, ideally camouflaged for its woodland habitat.

It may be asked how these winter and very early spring Geometer moths feed in view of the lack of nectar-bearing flowers at this time. In fact, most of them

THRUSHES

The vast numbers of hawthorns planted in British hedgerows in addition to those present naturally in great quantity in the woods and downland scrub, provide a rich food source for many birds in the form of their berries, known as 'haws'. In a good year the autumn crop can be exceptionally abundant and, in spite of huge numbers of hungry thrushes, like the fieldfares, redwings and song thrushes in John Davis's field studies opposite, can last well into the winter months. Among other nutrients, haws are rich in vitamin C and thus provide a sustaining food for birds and other animals.

Because winters in England, especially in the south, are generally milder than on the European mainland, many birds, such as fieldfares and redwings, migrate to us in the autumn in great numbers. Here they join our native resident thrushes, the blackbird, song thrush and mistle thrush, in feasting on the hawthorn berries. A walk in October or November along an extensive overgrown hedgerow laden with dark red haws may well be rewarded with the sight of all five species congregating together, with fieldfares and redwings by far the most numerous, although blackbird numbers may rival them.

If you sit quietly and unobtrusively, as the artist has done to obtain the sketches for his paintings, they will be so busy eating that they will take little notice of you. You can watch the speed with which they strip the haws off the branches and swallow them whole. Some get dropped, but are left for a ground-foraging bank vole or wood mouse to find. The seeds in the berries they eat are passed unharmed in their droppings and therefore widely dispersed – one reason why hawthorn spreads so rapidly far and wide.

As you watch them at close quarters, there will be good opportunities to notice their distinctive features: the chestnut-red patches on the flanks of the redwings, especially obvious when they fly, as they extend under the wings; the pronounced creamy-white eye stripe above the redwing's eye, so much more conspicuous than the weak suggestion of one in the song thrush; and the contrast between the grey head and chestnut brown back of the fieldfare, and between its blue-grey rump and black tail, so well displayed in the bird at right centre. The mistle thrush is not illustrated here, but although about the same size as the fieldfare, the more extensive black spotting on its underparts and lack of a blue-grey head and rump distinguish it.

As they feed, it is easy to pick out the occasional 'chack-chack-chack' of the fieldfares, the loud rattling chatter of a mistle thrush, the thin high-pitched 'tsip' calls of the song thrushes and the similar, but even thinner, higher and hissier 'tseeep' calls of the redwings. Towards dusk, as they settle down to roost in a hedgerow, one can sometimes hear the redwings indulging in a veritable chorus of sub-song.

have degenerate mouthparts, and are thus unable to feed; so their lives are short, rarely lasting more than a few days. The medium-sized December moth, like other members of the eggar family, to which it belongs, also has degenerate mouthparts and is unable to imbibe nectar; however, its life is not so short since it has a thick, 'furry' body which supplies all the energy it requires from the fat reserves stored up during its larval life. A common moth in wooded districts in south-east England, it is very hardy, flying with the onset of the first frosts in October and November, and continuing until mid-December. Both sexes are winged, the female being larger than the male, and readily visit artificial light sources. Their mainly sooty-brown forewings have reddish patches and pale cross-lines. The females lay their greyish eggs on the bark of a wide variety of deciduous trees, such as ash, elm, oak, poplar and hawthorn.

Another moth with a thickish body which flies in November and December and which is unable to take nectar is the plumed prominent. Occasionally, individuals of the night-flying angle shades and pearly underwing, and day-flying humming bird hawk-moth will be encountered during the winter months. All three species are well-known immigrants from the Mediterranean region (the angle shades is also resident) and, although those seen in this country in mild weather in winter may be the offspring of caterpillars which developed here in the summer or autumn, it is at least equally likely that they are fresh immigrants from continental Europe. All three species need nectar and, with the exception of the humming bird hawk, for which there is evidence of

Many of the winter-flying moths rely on their dull colouring as camouflage to avoid predators as there is little cover for them to hide in.

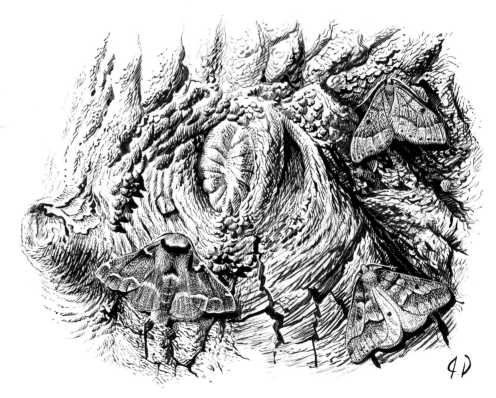

successful hibernation in the extreme south of England, they must soon die, unless they find sufficient flowers still in blossom.

By February, the last of the true winter-emerging moths will be overlapped by the earliest of the spring emergers, such as the spring usher, the pale brindled beauty, the small brindled beauty, the dotted border and the March moth. Of course, there are other kinds of insects, besides moths, which are active in winter; like the various species of winter gnats (Trichoceridae), quite harmless to man, which 'dance' in large swarms on winter afternoons, even after a snowfall. Moreover, mild, sunny days will tempt forth various other species of flies, beetles and so on from their hibernation sites, until a return to cold conditions forces them back again.

ROBIN'S PINCUSHION AND SIMILAR GALLS

The walker on the downs will almost certainly find bright red 'hairy' growths on the stems and twigs of dog roses as they are more obvious at this time of the year. These are bedeguar galls, more popularly known as robin's pincushions, a name that suits their appearance. They are caused by a small black gall wasp with a reddish abdomen, *Diplolepis rosae*, the female of which inserts her eggs in the rose between April and June. When they hatch the activity of the larvae causes the growing plant tissues to enlarge around them. Several wasp larvae feed in individual chambers inside the hard centre, sometimes 50 or more, plus, in many instances, a host of insect intruders – parasites, hyperparasites and others who are just there for the nutritious swollen plant-tissue feast. The galls are mature by the beginning of winter, and, if a few are collected and stored in a sterilized jar in a cold garage or shed, the inhabitants will emerge in the spring and can be released after study. Male *D. rosae* wasps are very rare, so the vast majority of those that emerge will be females. Almost all the females, therefore, lay their eggs without mating (parthenogenesis). Two closely related and very similar gall wasps, *D. eleganteriae* and *D. nervosus*, also cause galls on dog roses; but they are on the leaves and are much smaller than the robin's pincushions. The completely globular, pea-like ones are caused by *D. eleganteriae* and the similar ones with spikes, known as spiked pea galls, are the work of *D. nervosus*: both galls are green with a reddish tinge like an apple. All three types of galls are to be found in plenty throughout the North and South Downs.

DOWNLAND PLANTS IN WINTER

Although most plants have died down and few flowers are to be seen, there is still quite a lot of colour left over from autumn in the hedgerows and woods. Unless the icy grip of winter has struck early, and thrushes and other fruit-eating birds have been obliged to reap the berry harvest more completely than usual by mid-winter, there will still be bright red berries to be seen on the

161

hawthorns, dog roses, white and black bryonies, hollies, whitebeam, yews and other trees, plus the clusters of deep pink berries of the spindle. Mixed in with them here and there will be great masses of the fluffy, silver-grey down of traveller's joy, so rightly known to the countryman as old man's beard.

Other touches of colour will be found along the wood edges, in the hedgerows and on the open downland where those wild flowers which flower in the autumn or have a long season may still display a few blossoms – buttercups, dandelions, hawkweeds, scabiouses, chicory and so forth. Sometimes only a bloom or two will be found on each plant, providing a little nectar for any late flies or other insects which need it. There are, however, some wild plants which flower more or less all the year round, including winter, like chickweed, groundsel, red dead-nettle and common field speedwell; but their flowers, although attractive when closely examined, are small and inconspicuous, and they do not really bloom in earnest until March. There are a few plants, however, which have their chief period of flowering in late winter: these include the familiar snowdrops, winter aconite and winter heliotrope. Two plants typical of the calcareous woodlands, including those of the North and South Downs, may also begin flowering as early as January in mild winters; these are spurge-laurel and stinking hellebore.

January is the month, however, when the lemon-yellow male catkins, the lamb's tails of country children, open and hang on the hazels, and festoon miles of hedgerow and wood edge almost everywhere on the downs. The female catkins are erect and bud-like, and possess bright red, tassel-like styles; from them the nuts develop. By the autumn, the nuts, which are rich in protein and highly nutritious to man and animal alike, are ripe and much sought after by grey squirrels, dormice, wood mice and others, including various birds.

HARES AND RABBITS IN WINTER

Brown hares remain active throughout the winter and in especially mild years may even produce young at this time.

The brown hare is remarkably well adapted to surviving the rigours of even the harshest winters; even so, many do die, especially in severe winters. This is especially true in the case of leverets born in the autumn or in the winter – litters can be dropped at any time of the year, particularly in the milder south of England, where winter leverets are not uncommon. Adults and older young continue to feed, as they did earlier in the year, on grasses and the foliage of dandelions and similar wild plants still growing, but also feed on winter crops, such as turnip bulbs. In the course of a night adults may travel many miles to forage. Their thicker winter coat tends to be greyer than the summer one, otherwise there is not much difference. A fresh snowfall provides a good opportunity to follow their tracks; these can be distinguished from those of rabbits by their much larger size and, to some extent, by the habitat, since rabbits are unlikely to venture far from cover into a large field. The presence of the larger, slightly flattened, paler and more fibrous round faecal pellets of the brown hare provide another means of distinguishing its tracks from those of a

rabbit. In severe weather when it is difficult for both hares and rabbits to reach the vegetation beneath frozen snow and ice, they will instead strip the bark off trees, working upwards from the base and leaving the imprint of their large, paired upper incisors on the underlying wood. They obtain nutrition from the lower cambian layer of the bark, which may make the difference between life and death for them, but is, of course, very damaging to the trees. A thick snowfall will often allow rabbits to gnaw at low branches that otherwise would normally be out of their reach.

STOATS AND WEASELS

Young rabbits and hares (leverets) often fall prey to stoats and weasels, stoats also accounting for many adults as well; large rabbits are, however, too big for a weasel to overcome in the normal course of events and adult hares usually too large for either. Rabbits figure large in a stoat's diet, but it also attacks and eats many other animals; various birds and small mammals, including rats, and also, when these are scarce, lizards, frogs and large insects, and even berries. It hunts chiefly by scent, following its chosen victims relentlessly, and is extremely difficult for them to elude. Rabbits pursued by a stoat often become panic-stricken and paralysed with fear, squealing until they are killed by the usual deep bite at the back of the neck. As the writer has seen on the northern edge of the North Downs at Dartford, Kent, a stoat will sometimes perform strange

Stoat numbers are increasing again because of the increase in numbers of their main prey – rabbits.

antics attracting a large gathering of birds in the process: suddenly the stoat will cease its prancing and pounce on one of them in an instant.

Owing to their dependence on rabbits as a staple food, stoat numbers took a severe knock when the introduction of myxomatosis in 1953/54 almost wiped out the rabbit population in Britain. However, the surviving stoats managed to switch entirely to alternative prey, so that the population slowly recovered from about the 1960s onwards. Now that rabbit numbers are increasing, the stoat population's recovery has been more rapid in recent years. At the present time it occurs in at least small numbers almost everywhere on the North and South Downs. The stoat's distinctive black tail-tip is a good way of distinguishing it from a weasel even when quite young; the latter having a shorter tail without it. Another distinctive characteristic is the clear and sharp demarcation between the stoat's brown upper parts and its white underside; the weasel has a much more irregular demarcation line.

Like stoats, weasels normally have a bounding, snake-like gait, but when in a hurry they run extremely rapidly with their elongated bodies at full stretch; they are more nocturnal than stoats, but may be seen quite often in the daytime streaking across a path or road. They also hunt mainly by scent and kill their victims – chiefly mice, voles, young rabbits and other small mammals, frogs and small birds – by a bite at the back of the neck. Because of their small size, weasels are able to enter very small holes and chase small mammals along their underground runs and tunnels; they are also able to climb (for example, up to birds' nests and nesting boxes) and swim well, even catching the occasional fish.

The average life-span of a stoat is little more than a year and that of a weasel less than a year. Many of both species, especially young ones, die through lack of food in the winter; particularly when there is a population crash of one or other of the mammals on which they chiefly depend. Others are killed on the roads or at the hands of gamekeepers – you can still see here and there on the downs, rows of corpses of stoats, weasels, grey squirrels, magpies and other species hanging from gamekeepers' gibbets. In fact, by killing mice, voles, rats and rabbits, stoats and weasels are unintentionally doing much for the interests of man, notably farmers. They are not easy prey for natural predators but are sometimes killed by owls, buzzards, kestrels and foxes; weasels also falling prey to cats and occasionally to stoats. In spite of high annual mortality, weasels, like stoats, are well distributed throughout the North and South Downs, even close to cities like London, and appear to be more numerous than their ally.

FOXES IN WINTER

Mid-winter is mating time for the fox and this is described on page 142. Foxes, although primarily carnivorous, feed on a wide variety of foods. The list includes rabbits, squirrels, hedgehogs, smaller mammals, frogs, various larger beetles and other insects, birds and their eggs and young (including occasional game birds and poultry), earthworms, blackberries and other fruits, carrion and

165

household scraps. Food surplus to current needs is also buried, often conspicuously, for consumption later. Small prey, such as mice or voles, are stalked and pounced on with the forepaws, the fox rising up first on its hind legs. Initially it may detect these animals by the sound they make. The presence of foxes may be detected in the daytime by, among other things, their distinctive musty smell (once learnt), and by their faeces, which are usually pointed and twisted, and frequently linked together by the undigested hairs of their prey. The latter are usually deposited in prominent places, such as on molehills, and are very dark when fresh.

Foxes slowly moult during the summer and by the autumn have developed a thick and handsome coat of fur. By this time, too, the cubs have become more or less adult and, while some vixens remain with the family group until the following year, the remainder and the dog-foxes will have dispersed by January, the latter to establish their own territories. Many of these young foxes

are run over and killed on the roads in this period; and, of course, many others in rural situations, such as the downlands, lose their lives at the hands of man in one way or another. Urban and suburban-living foxes have less to fear from man, town-dwellers being usually more tolerant of them and even appreciative. Foxes adapt to almost all types of habitat, especially if the countryside has a mosaic pattern and food is plentiful: the North and South Downs satisfy these requirements, and they are therefore more or less common everywhere.

WINTER SURVIVAL OF BIRDS OF PREY

The large amount of carrion in the form of road casualties is undoubtedly a blessing for young and inexperienced crows and other corvids at times of food shortages; they become adept at dodging passing vehicles. Sometimes, at the

Hen harrier, kestrel and sparrow hawk over Lychpole Hill near Steyning. In a hard winter, the raptor population in the south of England will be augmented by birds from farther north, where food is more difficult to find.

extreme western end of the South Downs, where scattered pairs breed, and occasionally elsewhere in the area of the North and South Downs in winter, buzzards also take advantage in early morning of the carnage on the roads. An increasing breeding species in England, buzzards may gradually recolonize the downland haunts they lost in Kent and Sussex during the nineteenth century.

A moderately large raptor which often winters in south-east England and is quite frequently seen on the downs at this season, especially the South Downs, is the hen harrier. They come from their breeding grounds in northern Britain and possibly also from Scandinavia where the breeding population does not overwinter. Judging by hen harriers seen flying in from the sea along the Kent and Sussex coasts in autumn, some birds arrive from breeding areas in France. On the South Downs, wintering hen harriers are likely to be seen buoyantly quartering low over open terrain almost anywhere along their length, but are most often reported from such favoured bird-watching areas as Beachy Head, the Arun and Cuckmere Valleys, Pulborough Brooks, Cissbury, Seaford and Lullington Heath. In Kent they are most often reported along the North Kent marshes, below the dip slope of the North Downs, but are also occasionally seen on the downs themselves, notably where the River Stour cuts through the chalk, and might possibly be reported more often if more observers worked the downs. Their winter food consists mainly of young hares and rabbits, many voles and other small mammals, and sometimes small birds, which may be captured on the wing.

Another overwintering raptor, which the sharp-eyed observer may encounter on the downs, is the small and dashing merlin, a falcon whose male is little bigger than a blackbird and looks rather like a sparrow hawk in general appearance and colour scheme; however, it has the characteristic sharp-pointed wings of a typical falcon. The mainly brown female is larger, being almost the size of a kestrel, but with a shorter tail. Like the hen harrier, it breeds mostly in northern Britain and Wales, with a few pairs also nesting on Exmoor. Many of these northern birds move south for the winter, especially to coastal areas, their numbers being supplemented by merlins from Scandinavia and even Iceland. As is usual, therefore, most birds are reported along the coastal marshes and at such places as Beachy Head, where the South Downs meet the sea, although some are seen farther inland on the downs around, for example, Lewes and Lullington. Here they may be seen pursuing, with great agility and tenacity, the small birds like larks and pipits on which they chiefly prey. Their normal flight is swift and erratic, wing-beats alternating with short glides as they hug the contours of the land closely and thus frequently disappear from sight.

Winter is often as hard a season for birds of prey as for other animals when food may become scarce. It is especially so for immature birds whose inexperience and inefficiency in securing live prey, particularly in bad weather, is frequently too much for them. Thus, as is usually the case with wild animals, a much higher proportion of immature raptors fail to survive the winter than the more experienced adults. In prolonged spells of severe cold, snow cover and frost, kestrels, merlins, sparrow hawks and other raptors may be forced to follow the hard weather movements of the birds on which they prey to milder parts of the country. In an average winter, however, the resident kestrels and sparrow hawks hunting on and around the North and South Downs are reinforced by others from farther north in Britain and from the Continent, and they therefore appear commoner than at other seasons of the year.

WINTERING WILDFOWL

Where river valleys bisect the North and South Downs there is plenty of bird-life to be seen on a winter walk. The valleys of the Arun in West Sussex and the Cuckmere River in East Sussex are particularly fine examples of these. The Cuckmere, with its shingle bank-blocked exit to the sea at Cuckmere Haven, lies below downs crowned to the east by Friston Forest, and forms part of the Seven Sisters Country Park. The ancient meanders of the river have been cut off by a straight channel and the upper saltmarshes drained, but the old saltmarsh creeks can still be seen from the downland slopes. Lower down towards the river mouth there is still some saltmarsh remaining; both this and the shingle bank have a rich flora.

Near the river mouth a lagoon was constructed in 1975, and this is a favoured feeding and resting area for waders and waterfowl at migration times as well as in the winter. Wintering birds here and on the saltmarsh and reclaimed marsh pasture of the lower river include Canada geese, brent geese, shelduck, teal, wigeon, goosanders, ringed plovers, golden plovers, grey plovers, lapwings, dunlin, jack snipe, snipe, curlew, redshank, greenshank, lesser and great black-backed gulls, hen harriers and merlins.

In West Sussex, the valley and floodplain of the River Arun has already been described in the 'Summer' chapter and reference made to the wildfowl wintering there, particularly for the adjacent nature reserves of Amberley Wild Brooks, Waltham Brooks (both Sussex Wildlife Trust) and Pulborough Brooks (Royal Society for the Protection of Birds). All attract flocks of Bewick's and mute swans, Canada, grey lag and white-fronted geese, shelduck, teal, wigeon, shoveler, pintail, pochard, tufted duck, lapwing, dunlin, ruff, snipe, curlew and redshank, especially when the pasture fields are flooded. Wintering birds of prey include hen harriers, buzzards, merlins, peregrine falcons, and short-eared owls. Careful habitat management by the Sussex Wildlife Trust and the RSPB has already substantially increased the populations of birds wintering there and they are to be congratulated. With the return of spring, the Brooks resound to the courtship displays of increasing numbers of breeding lapwings, redshanks and snipe.

NATURE
RESERVES
AND AREAS OF INTEREST

T he following selection of places to visit on the North and South Downs includes wildlife reserves for which entrance fees may be charged or a permit required as well as other sites where public access is unrestricted. They are listed in alphabetical order under counties and each entry gives, where known, the name of the authority or organization owning or managing the site, the distance from the nearest sizeable town or towns, a national Grid map reference taken from the appropriate Ordnance Survey 2 cm to 1 km Landranger map (how to read it is explained on the map) and wildlife items of particular interest. If it is situated on or near the North or South Downs Ways (national long-distance trails) this is also stated.

Where permits for visits are known to be necessary, this is indicated in the entry; applications should be made as early as possible to the appropriate authority (see address section). Car parks are also mentioned in the entries where they are known to exist, but readers are warned that some may be incapable of accommodating more than a few cars. In parking elsewhere every consideration should be given to the convenience of local residents. Fees may be chargeable at some official car parks. Dogs are unlikely to be welcome on a nature reserve and should be kept completely under control where allowed, especially in the vicinity of livestock. Finally, when visiting reserves or privately owned land, visitors should be careful to keep to the recognized paths or rights of way.

The following abbreviations are used in the gazetteer:

BBCS   The British Butterfly Conservation Society
BC   The appropriate Borough Council
CAR   Car parking available (may be limited)
CC   The appropriate County Council
DC   The appropriate Local District Council
EN   English Nature (formerly the Nature Conservancy Council)
FC   The Forestry Commission
FSC   The Field Studies Council

HWT   The Hampshire & Isle of Wight Naturalists' Trust
INF   Information Centre
km   Kilometre(s)
KTNC   The Kent Trust for Nature Conservation
LNHS   The London Natural History Society
LNR   Local Nature Reserve
m   Mile(s)
NCC   The Nature Conservancy Council (now English Nature)
NDW   The North Downs Way
NNR   National Nature Reserve
NR   Nature Reserve
NT   The National Trust
NTR   Nature Trail
P   Open to the public or viewable from paths and roads
PER   Permit required
PER/A Permit required for areas away from rights of way
RSPB   The Royal Society for the Protection of Birds
SDW   The South Downs Way
SSSI   Site of Special Scientific Interest
SWT   The Surrey Wildlife Trust
SXWT   The Sussex Wildlife Trust

HAMPSHIRE

ALRESFORD VALLEY AND DOWNS
SU5833
Near Alresford, 7 m ENE of Winchester. P
(use Wayferer's Way footpath on Downs).
CAR (near Old Alresford Pond). River
Alre (clear chalk stream) and adjacent chalk
downs. Reed and sedge warblers, reed
buntings, kingfisher, little grebe, tufted
duck, redshank, snipe and water rail in
river valley, with crayfish in river.
Lapwing, golden plover (winter), corn
bunting and yellowhammer on downs.

BUTSER HILL AND QUEEN ELIZABETH
COUNTRY PARK
SU7221
W side of A3, 3 m SSW of Petersfield.
CC. P. CAR (fee). On SDW. Butser
Ancient Farm. Butser Hill 271 metres
(889 ft) high. Chalk downland with some
scrub, partly cultivated. Fine chalk flora

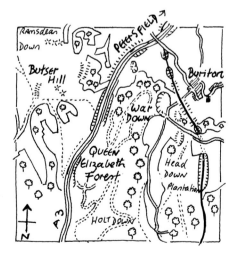

and associated insects. Grey partridge,
kestrel, sparrow hawk, common gull
(winter), ring ouzel, wheatear, whinchat
(on passage).

OLD WINCHESTER HILL
SU640205
Near Corhampton, 7 m WSW of
Petersfield. NNR. EN. P. On SDW. Iron
Age camp. Herb-rich chalk grassland with
round-headed rampion and all vegetational
stages to yew climax woodland. Juniper
scrub also present. Butterflies: silver-
spotted skipper, chalk-hill blue, small b.
Duke of Burgundy fritillary, marbled
white. Rufous grasshopper.

QUEEN ELIZABETH FOREST PARK AND
WAR DOWN
SU718182
3 m SSW of Petersfield, E side of A3. FC.
P. CAR (fee). INF. NTR. On SDW.
Broad-leaved and coniferous woodland on
chalk downland. Golden pheasant, turtle
dove, woodpeckers, willow tit and
warblers.

ST CATHERINE'S HILL
SU485275
1 m S of Winchester city centre. HWT. P.
SSSI. Iron Age fort. Chalk grassland and
scrub with good flora including kidney and
horseshoe vetches, autumn lady's-tresses,
bee, frog, pyramidal and southern marsh
orchids, devil's bit scabious, clustered
bellflower. Insects include chalk-hill blue
butterfly and long-winged conehead bush-
cricket.

Turtle doves.

SELBORNE HANGER AND COMMON
SU735337
3 m SE of Alton. NT. P. Beech hanger and
common on chalk downland made famous
by Gilbert White, eighteenth-century
parson-naturalist. Selborne Common
consists of beech and oak woodland,
grassland, scrub and heath. Chalk flora
includes stinking hellebore, spurge-laurel,
mezereon, yellow bird's-nest, bird's-nest
orchid, twayblade, broad-leaved
helleborine. Butterflies: green hairstreak,
holly blue and speckled wood. Birds:
woodcock, turtle dove, woodpeckers,
marsh tit, nightingale, grasshopper
warbler, wood warbler and hawfinch.
Badger and fox.

WINNALL MOORS NR. WINCHESTER
SU4931
1 m N of city centre. HWT. P. CAR.
Former water meadows abandoned in
1930s bordering famous chalk stream
(River Itchen) rich in lime; now grazed hay
meadows. Crayfish, trout, salmon, bank
and water voles, tufted duck, pochard, little
grebe, redpoll, siskin, reed and sedge
warblers, reed and corn buntings.
Swallows, starlings and pied wagtails roost
in reed-beds. Green-flowered helleborine.

KENT

BOXLEY HILL AND WOOD
TQ775596

2 m N of Maidstone. P. On NDW. Mixed woodland on downland escarpment with native box, beech and yew, and good chalk flora.

CHALLOCK FOREST
TR020503

Near Charing, about 5 m N of Ashford. FC. NTR in King's Wood. P. On NDW. CAR. Mixed woodland with beech, yew and much sweet chestnut coppice on downland plateau. Fallow deer, nightjar.

DARENT VALLEY
TQ5260

Chalk stream (River Darent) flowing N through gap in North Downs from Otford, near Sevenoaks, to the Thames N of Dartford and bordered by a variety of uncultivated and cultivated chalk downland habitats. Recommended section is between Otford and Horton Kirby, especially around Farningham, Eynsford, Lullingstone, Shoreham and Magpie Bottom. Fine chalk flora including bee, fragrant, early marsh, pyramidal and common spotted orchids, yellow-wort, spurge-laurel, carline thistle, kidney and horseshoe vetches, sainfoin and viper's bugloss. Butterflies include chalk-hill blue, brown argus, green and white-letter hairstreaks, silver-washed fritillary, white admiral and ringlet. Moths include five- and six-spotted burnets and chalk carpet. Badger, fox, common lizard and adder. Roman snail. Crayfish in river. Lapwing, grey partridge, kestrel, sparrow hawk, turtle dove, willow tit, tree pipit, redpoll, siskin and yellowhammer.

DOWNE (IN GREATER LONDON)
TQ432616

(a) Darwin's Orchid Bank. 3 m SW of Orpington. KTNC. PER. Grassy bank with fine chalk flora including several species of orchids studied by Charles Darwin. Surrounded by beech wood.

(b) Charles Darwin Memorial Museum (open afternoons Wednesday–Sunday, fee). Home for 40 years of the famous biologist/naturalist and author of *The Origin of Species* with charming garden, including his 'thinking path'.

FOLKESTONE WARREN
TR2838

Lies below cliff-top village of Capel-le-Ferne, 4 m NE of Folkestone, 3 m SW of Dover. DC. P. On NDW. Well known for its unusual insect fauna, including such moths as Bond's wainscot, dew moth, feathered ranunculus, fiery clearwing, the restharrow and sub-angled wave; also 13 species of Orthoptera, including grey bush-cricket, stripe-winged and rufous grasshoppers. Habitat consists of chalk turf and cliffs, swampy depressions and scrub on clay beside the railway track.

LYDDEN AND STONEWALL
TR 2645

Approx. $2\frac{1}{2}$ m. NW of Dover. Near NDW. SSSI. Chalk grassland escarpment, both ungrazed and grazed, with some scrub and mixed woodland. Includes Lydden Nature Reserve of KTNC. P. CAR (limited). Rich flora (includes autumn lady's-tresses, burnt, early spider and fragrant orchids, chalk milkwort and squinancywort) and insect fauna (adonis blue, marbled white and silver-spotted skipper butterflies

Roe hind.

and 14 species of Orthoptera including wart-biter and great green bush-crickets, stripe-winged and mottled grasshoppers). Breeding linnets and yellowhammers.

PARK GATE DOWN NR
TR168459

1 m NW of Elham, near Lyminge Forest; midway between Canterbury and Folkestone. KTNC. P. CAR (limited). Rich chalk grassland flora on slopes; down capped with heavy clay. Plants include bee, common spotted, early purple, fragrant, monkey, musk and pyramidal orchids, columbine and hairy violet. Brown argus, marbled white and Essex skipper butterflies. Adder and common lizard.

QUEENDOWN WARREN LNR
TQ827629

5 m W of Sittingbourne, between villages of Hartlip, Bredhurst and Yelsted. KTNC. P (access restricted to Main Bank). CAR. Open chalk grassland and scrub, plus coppiced mixed woodland. Some clay-with-flints in places. A captive rabbit warren in medieval times. Rich chalk flora including such orchids as bee, early spider, fragrant, greater butterfly and man, also horseshoe vetch, sainfoin, rock-rose and yellow-wort. Butterflies include adonis and chalk-hill blues, brown argus and marbled white. Adder. Dormouse. Yellowhammer.

TEMPLE EWELL DOWNS
TR275454

4 m NW of Dover. CC. P. Near NDW. Chalk grass and scrub. Fine flora and associated insects, including good range of chalk butterflies.

WYE AND CRUNDALE DOWNS
TR079455

Between Wye & Hastingleigh, 5 m NE of Ashford. NNR. EN (NCC). P. PER/A. CAR. On NDW. NTR. Large area of chalk grass downland with scrub and large woodland. Rich chalk flora with 17 species of orchids, including fly, lady and musk, also chalk and Kentish milkworts. Insects include 27 species of butterflies and rufous grasshopper. Sparrow hawk, tawny owl, lesser whitethroat, nightingale and hawfinch among breeding birds. Adder.

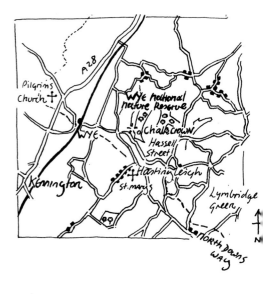

YOCKLETTS BANK NR
TR125467

8 m S of Canterbury. KTNC. P. CAR. Woodland on chalk downland capped with clay-with-flints. Fine flora includes beech, hornbeam, field maple, wayfaring tree, spindle, spurge-laurel, broad-leaved and white helleborine, common spotted, early purple, fly, greater butterfly, lady and pyramidal orchids. Birds include nightingale, tree creeper and tawny owl. Badger.

Surrey

Banstead Downs (Park Downs)
TQ2757

About 4 m SE of Epsom. DC. P. Scrub and birch increasing on once open downland. Butterflies include brown argus, small blue, chalk-hill blue (known here since at least 1704!). Birds include tree pipit and, on passage, pied flycatcher.

Betchworth Hills
TQ207519

2 m N of Betchworth, between Dorking and Reigate. P. Near NDW. Good exposure of chalk strata in the large quarry. Round-headed rampion and early gentian.

Bookham Common
TQ1256

2½ m W of Leatherhead. NT. P. Wooded common with much oak, mainly on London clay, but with varied habitats. One of the most closely observed places in Britain, having been studied in detail by the LNHS annually since 1941. Varied flora and associated insect communities, including white admiral butterfly. Breeding birds include marsh and willow tits, wood warbler and nightingale.

Box Hill
TQ179513

1 m NE of Dorking. NT. P. On NDW. CAR. FSC Centre at Juniper Hall. Open

Brimstone butterfly.

chalk downland with beech, box and yew hangers and characteristic chalk flora (various orchids, etc.) and insects (brown argus, chalk-hill blue and dark green fritillary butterflies; common green, mottled, rufous and stripe-winged grasshoppers). Beech and oak dominated mixed woodland on clay-with-flints with some calcifuge plants. For detailed account of ecology see Lousley (1950).

Dawcombe (Wood) NR
TQ213526

2 m WNW of Reigate, 3 m NE of Dorking. SWT. PER. Near NDW. Mixed woodland with thick hawthorn scrub and some open down on steep chalk scarp slope. Rich chalk flora includes bee, common spotted, fly, fragrant, greater butterfly, man and pyramidal orchids. Mixed woodland contains ash, beech, field maple, spindle and whitebeam. Fine invertebrate fauna, also common lizard, slow worm, badger, fox, rabbit and roe deer. Nearly 60 species of birds recorded.

Epsom Common and Downs and Walton Downs
TQ2257

P. CAR. Racecourse and open grass chalk downs. Good calcareous flora with cypress

and twiggy spurges, and early gentian. Insects include small blue butterfly. Birds recorded include grey and red-legged partridges, willow tit, tree pipit, nightingale, stonechat, grasshopper warbler, wood warbler, redpoll and siskin.

HOG'S BACK
SU9048 and SU9248
Between Farnham and Guildford. CC 'open space'. P. Near NDW. Steep scarp and dip slopes with good chalk flora (yew, whitebeam, wayfaring tree, wild privet, traveller's joy, hairy violet, kidney vetch, autumn gentian and round-headed rampion) and associated insects.

HOWELL HILL LNR
TQ238621
Off A232 near Sutton and Cheam. SWT. CAR (nearby side roads). Old chalk spoil heaps with grassland and scrub; good chalk flora showing succession from bare chalk to woodland. Plants include broomrapes, kidney vetch, mouse-eared hawkweed, bee, common spotted and pyramidal orchids. Good invertebrate fauna with green hairstreak and small blue butterflies. Green woodpeckers feed at the many ant-hills.

NEWLANDS CORNER AND SILENT POOL
TQ0449
Adjacent to Albury Downs, 3 m E of Guildford. CC 'open space'. P. On NDW.

CAR. W end of some 7 m of well-preserved chalk escarpment, stretching to Ranmore. Broad-leaved woodland and scrub. Tree pipits. Roe deer.

NORBURY PARK
TQ1654
Between Dorking and Leatherhead. CC 'open space'. P. Beech woods with box and yew. Wood warblers.

POLESDEN LACEY
TQ140533
1½ m S of Great Bookham, 1½ m NNW of Dorking. NT. P. Near NDW. Beech woods on dip slope of North Downs. Wood warblers.

RANMORE COMMON AND DENBIES HILLSIDE
TQ1450
2 m WNW of Dorking. NT. P. On NDW. Marked contrast between calcareous flora of chalk escarpment (Denbies) and non-calcareous flora on wooded clay-with-flints of the downland plateau. Chalk flora includes several orchid species. Adonis blue and silver-spotted skipper are among butterflies occurring.

REIGATE AND COLLEY HILLS
TQ2552
NT. P. On NDW. Open grassland on chalk escarpment and scrub and beech woods on downland plateau. Views to South Downs. Fine chalk flora including round-headed rampion and ground-pine.

SEALE CHALK-PIT, HOG'S BACK
SU899482
3 m E of Farnham, just NE of Seale, below A31 on Hog's Back. SWT. PER. Near NDW. Old chalk quarry on steep S-facing escarpment slope of Hog's Back with section showing steep monoclinal dip of the chalk strata. Good chalk flora with common spotted, fly and twayblade orchids, plus spindle and wild privet.

EAST SUSSEX

BEACHY HEAD
TV5995

1 m SW of Eastbourne. Part of Seven Sisters Heritage Coast. P. On SDW. Chalk downland and sea cliffs. Fine chalk flora with maritime element including rock samphire, sea beet, slender-headed thistle, dwarf spurge, autumn gentian and round-headed rampion. Migrant birds and insects. Popular with bird-watchers for sea-watching.

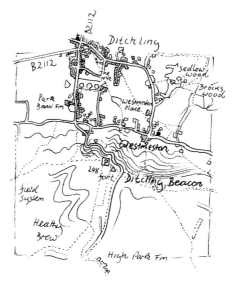

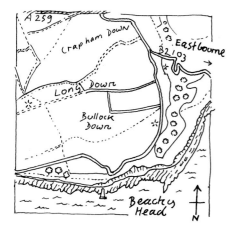

CASTLE HILL NNR AND KINGSTON SCARP
TV3707

Kingston near Lewes, 2 m SW of Lewes, NNR (EN). P. Near SDW. Complex of grazed grassland and gorse and other scrub on steep coombes extending from Newmarket Hill to Iford Hill. Some secondary grassland on former cultivated land and leached areas near slope summits. Rich chalk flora and associated insect communities, including nearly 30 species of butterflies (adonis and chalk-hill blues, etc.) and 13 species of Orthoptera (wart-biter, long-winged conehead, stripe-winged and mottled grasshoppers). Ring ouzel among birds regular on migration.

CUCKMERE HAVEN – SEE SEVEN SISTERS COUNTRY PARK

Wart-biter.

DITCHLING BEACON
TQ332132

5 m N of Brighton, above Ditchling. NT. P. CAR. Also LNR of SXWT. Steep chalk down escarpment with all stages of plant succession represented from calcareous grassland through mixed scrub to ash woodland. Arable land on downland plateau to S. Rich chalk flora with round-headed rampion, yellow-wort, fairy flax, rock-rose, kidney vetch, common twayblade, bee, man and other orchids, dropwort and squinancywort. Chalk-hill blue, brown argus, green hairstreak, marbled white and ringlet butterflies. Breeding birds are green woodpecker, jay, whitethroat, meadow pipit, linnet, corn bunting and yellowhammer.

FRISTON FOREST, WESTDEAN
TV526996

2 m E of Seaford, 4 m W of Eastbourne.
FC. P. On SDW. CAR. NTR through
beech and conifer plantations on
downland. Best for bird-watching:
woodcock, sparrow hawk, turtle dove,
green and great spotted woodpeckers, coal,
long-tailed and marsh tits. Butterflies
include marbled white, ringlet and hedge
brown. Plants along forest rides include
centaury, cowslip, dropwort, red bartsia
and viper's bugloss.

White helleborine

LULLINGTON HEATH AND DEEP COOMBE
TQ5202 and TQ5302

5 m NW of Eastbourne, 4 m NE of
Seaford. NNR (EN). P. PER/A. On
SDW. CAR (limited). Chalk downland
with grazed and ungrazed grassland, gorse
and other dense scrub, and chalk heath with
ling on clay and blown sand. Calcareous
and calcifuge flora. Insect communities
include butterflies, bush-crickets and
grasshoppers of the chalk; notably the
wart-biter and long-winged conehead
bush-crickets, mottled and stripe-winged
grasshoppers. Among breeding birds are
Dartford and grasshopper warblers,
nightingale, tree pipit, corn bunting,
yellowhammer, turtle dove, grey and red-
legged partridges. Visitors include ring
ouzel, hobby, merlin, buzzard, hen harrier
and woodcock.

MALLING DOWN NR
TQ423107

Above South Malling, 1 m NE of Lewes.
SXWT. SSSI. P. Car. Near SDW. Steep
chalk grassland slopes, thick scrub, deep
coombe, dew pond and disused chalk-pits.
Ancient field system, long barrow and
tumuli. Grassland has fine chalk flora with
autumn gentian, round-headed rampion,
dropwort, horseshoe and kidney vetches
and various orchids. Butterflies include
adonis and chalk-hill blues and marbled
white.

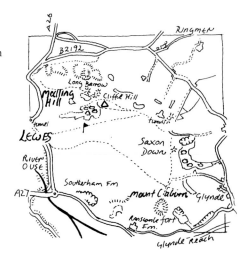

178

Mount Caburn
TQ444090

2 m ESE of Lewes. P. Near SDW. Ancient hill-top fort on summit of chalk down with some scrub and woodland. Formerly sheep-grazed, now replaced by cattle. Much ploughed up in recent years. Flora includes scarce sweetbriar. Some chalk-hill blue butterflies – adonis blue and silver-spotted skipper formerly.

Seaford Head LNR
TV5197

Seaford. Chalk downland and sea cliffs, narrow coombe with scrub, shingle beach. Fine flora. Migrant birds include ring ouzel and black redstart.

Seven Sisters Country Park
TV5199

6 m W of Eastbourne, 2 m E of Seaford. CC. P. CAR. Near SDW. SSSI. Cuckmere River valley, shingle beach, saltmarsh pasture, chalk downs and sea cliffs. Varied flora includes common spotted, early purple and pyramidal orchids, round-headed rampion, viper's bugloss, autumn gentian, field fleawort, carline thistle, small hare's-ear, moon carrot, rock sea-lavender, hoary stock, sea cabbage, sea aster and yellow horned-poppy. Downland insects include chalk-hill blue and marbled white butterflies, emperor and oak eggar moths, great green bush-cricket. Lesser marsh grasshopper on saltmarsh. Among birds, fulmars and jackdaws breed on the cliffs, little owls, meadow pipits, skylarks and stonechats on the downs, and shelduck, ringed plovers, redshanks and reed buntings in the valley. Ring ouzels, wheatears, pied flycatchers, black redstarts, merlins, hen and marsh harriers can be seen on passage.

Green woodpecker.

West Sussex

Amberley Wild Brooks SSSI
TQ0314
Immediately N of Amberley, 3 m SW of Pulborough, 4 m. N of Arundel. PER for access to very small SXWT reserves; rest accessible by public footpath. Near SDW. Alluvial floodplain on E bank of River Arun with rich aquatic and marsh flora and fauna, consisting of marsh pasture, scrub and woodland intersected by drainage dykes. Fields of great tussock sedge. Breeding birds include snipe, redshank, lapwing and yellow wagtail. Often flooded in winter and visited by wigeon, teal, shoveler, pochard, Bewick's swan, hen harrier, short-eared owl, etc.

Arundel Park
TQ0208
P. Near SDW. CAR. Chalk downland with ancient broad-leaved woodland and recent plantations. Fine flora and associated insect and bird communities. Notable plants include large cuckoo-pint, caper spurge, stinking hellebore and stinking iris. Insects include long-winged conehead, stripe-winged, rufous and woodland grasshoppers.

Barlavington Down
SU965155
Above Barlavington, near Duncton; 4 m S of Petworth. P. Near SDW. Open chalk grassland with scrub and in Barlavington Hanger, a good example of a hanging wood.

Cissbury Ring (Hill)
TQ140082
3 m N of Worthing. NT. P. CAR. Near SDW. Also Lychpole Hill. Chalk grassland and scrub, with Neolithic flint-mines within earthworks of the Ring. Much of surrounding downland cultivated, with scattered elder, blackthorn and hawthorn scrub and small woods. Fine flora and

associated insects. Good bird-watching area, especially at migration times when flycatchers, warblers, chats, redstarts and ring ouzels funnel through scrub in valley bottoms and on slopes. Hobbies, marsh and Montagu's harriers also appear on migration, while in winter buzzards, hen harriers and short-eared owls occur. Breeding species include grey and red-legged partridges, lapwings, kestrels, turtle and stock doves, green woodpeckers, linnets, corn buntings and yellowhammers.

DUNCTON CHALK-PIT NR
SU960163

4 m SSW of Petworth, 5 m SE of Midhurst. ¾ m S of Duncton. P. SXWT. Near SDW. Disused chalk-pit below beech hanger on escarpment of Duncton Hill. Good chalk flora with deadly nightshade, ploughman's spikenard, wild liquorice and various orchids, plus rich insect communities.

KINGLEY VALE NNR
SU824088

4 m NW of Chichester on A286. NNR. EN (NCC). PER/A. P. CAR. NTR. Chalk valley with open turf downland slopes, dense scrub, huge natural yew woodland (probably finest in Europe) and chalk heath on downland plateau. Splendid flora with much hairy violet and associated insect

fauna. 34 species of butterflies breed, including grizzled skipper, chalk-hill blue, dark green, pearl-bordered and small pearl-bordered fritillaries, purple emperor, white admiral, hedge brown and ringlet. Birds also good, with long-eared and tawny owls, hobby, grasshopper warbler and other warblers, tree pipit and hawfinch. Buzzards and woodcock occur in winter and black redstarts, pied flycatchers, etc., on migration. Wild fallow deer present.

LEVIN DOWN NR
SU888131

SE side of Levin Down above villages of Charlton and Singleton, 5 m NNE of Chichester. SSSI. SXWT. P. Near SDW. Nearly 27 hectares (67 acres) of steep S and E facing chalk downland surrounded by arable land and woodland. Mixture of open grassland with chalk flora (autumn lady's-tresses, clustered bellflower, horseshoe and kidney vetches, marjoram and thyme); chalk heath with ling; scrub and large colony of junipers. Insects include such butterflies as chalk-hill blue and brown argus.

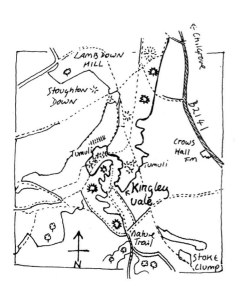

MILL HILL, SHOREHAM
TQ212067

Immediately N of A27 at Old Shoreham P. Chalk downland overlooking River Adur. Good chalk flora and insect fauna, including chalk-hill and adonis blue butterflies.

PULBOROUGH BROOKS NR
TQ0517

Below South Downs escarpment S of Pulborough, immediately N of Amberley Wild Brooks (see entry). RSPB. PER. Near SDW. Part of floodplain of River Arun, plus adjacent farmland and woodland. Wetland flora includes flowering rush, frogbit, greater water parsnip and yellow water-lily. Breeding birds include lapwing, snipe, redshank and nightingales; winter vistors: Bewick's swan, wigeon, teal, shoveler, pintail, hen harrier, short-eared owl, etc. Other animals include the club-tailed dragonfly, red-eyed and variable damselflies and grass snakes.

SADDLESCOMBE CHALK-PIT NR
TQ268122

5 m NW of Brighton, between Poynings and Saddlescombe. SSSI. BC and SXWT. CAR. On SDW. Disused chalk-pit with junipers, orchids and other chalk plants.

WALTHAM BROOKS NR
TQ026159

Coldwaltham on A29, 2½ m SW of Pulborough. Below South Downs escarpment. SSSI. SXWT. P. Near SDW. Marsh pasture with standing water beside River Arun and part of its floodplain. Adjacent and similar to Amberley Wild Brooks and Pulborough Brooks (see entries).

WEST DEAN WOODS NR
SU844153

4 m N of Chichester, near A286 and West Dean village. SSSI. SXWT. PER. Near SDW. Fragment of primeval woodland which once covered South Downs. Former hazel and oak standard coppicing cycle restored. Good woodland flora with wild daffodils, primroses, violets and early purple orchids, etc. Butterflies include pearl-bordered fritillary, and nightingale is among birds breeding.

Rooks.

Maps

For exploring the North and South Downs the Landranger series of Ordnance Survey maps 2 cm to 1 km (1¼ inches to 1 mile) are ideal: maps 176 to 179, 185 to 189 and 196 to 199 cover the entire area. For an overview of the whole region the Ordnance Survey's Routemaster 9 South East England 1 cm to 2.5 km (1 inch to 1 mile) and the RAC Road Map of the South East 1 inch to 3 miles are good. The latter also shows the routes of the North and South Downs Ways.

Useful addresses

The addresses of county and local natural history and ornithological societies tend to change frequently as the post of Hon. Secretary is usually filled by volunteer members; therefore these are listed, but not provided with an address unless it is known to be a permanent one. The current address can normally be obtained from local public libraries or by sending a *stamped addressed envelope* to the appropriate county wildlife trust (addresses below).

British Butterfly Conservation Society, P.O. Box 222, Dedham, Colchester, Essex, CO7 6IY

British Trust for Ornithology, The Nunnery, Nunnery Place, Thetford, Norfolk, 1P24 2PU

Countryside Commission, South East Region, 4th Floor, 71 Kingsway, London, WC2B 6ST

English Nature (ex NCC), Northminster House, Peterborough, Northamptonshire, PE1 1UA

English Nature South East Region, Coldharbour Farm, Wye, Ashford, Kent, TN25 5DB

Field Studies Council, Preston Montford, Montford Bridge, Shrewsbury, Shropshire, SY4 1HW

Field Studies Council, Juniper Hall Field Centre, Dorking, Surrey, RH5 6DA

Forestry Commission, East Region: Great Eastern House, Tenison Road, Cambridge, CB1 2DU

Hampshire and Isle of Wight Wildlife Trust, 71 The Hundred, Romsey, Hampshire, SO5 8BZ

Hampshire Ornithological Society

Kent Ornithological Society

Kent Trust for Nature Conservation, The Annex, 1a Bower Mount Road, Maidstone, Kent, ME16 8AX

London Natural History Society

London Wildlife Trust, 80 York Way, London, N1 9AG

National Trust, 36 Queen Anne's Gate, London, SW1H 9AS

Nature Conservancy Council (see English Nature)

Royal Society for the Prevention of Cruelty to Animals, The Causeway, Horsham, West Sussex, RH12 1HG

Royal Society for the Protection of Birds, The Lodge, Sandy, Bedfordshire, SG19 2DL

RSPB South East Regional Office, 8 Church Street, Shoreham, West Sussex, BN43 5DQ

The Surrey Wildlife Trust, Powell Corderoy Annexe, Longfield Road, Dorking, Surrey, RH4 3DF

Sussex Wildlife Trust, Woods Mill, Henfield, West Sussex, BN5 9BR

Badger

BIBLIOGRAPHY

Nobody in these days of great advances in knowledge can claim to know everything about even a single subject, let alone one as all-embracing as natural history. It is inevitable, therefore, that in a book as wide-ranging as this in its coverage of the animals and plants inhabiting the North and South Downs, and even allowing for his broad interests and personal familiarity with this subject, the writer has found it necessary to consult the work of others, particularly in those specialized areas where their expertise and experience is greater than his own, and to whom he makes grateful acknowledgement through this bibliography. Nevertheless, while careful to check all his facts and statements, he has drawn upon nearly fifty years of personal field observation and studies.

It has not been possible to give all the source references here that I would have wished, so a full list has been deposited, together with a copy of the book, in the Library of the Zoological Society of London and is thus accessible to anyone wishing to consult it.

Brown, R. W., Lawrence, M. J. and Pope, J. (1984) *The Country Life Guide to Animals of Britain and Europe their tracks, trails and signs*, Country Life Books, Newnes Books, Feltham, Middlesex.

Burton, J. (1968) *The Oxford Book of Insects*, Oxford University Press, Oxford.

Burton, R. M. (1983) *Flora of the London Area*, London Natural History Society, London.

Campbell, B. (1964) *The Oxford Book of Birds*, Oxford University Press, Oxford.

Campbell, B. and Ferguson-Lees (1972) *A Field Guide to Birds' Nests*, Constable, London.

Carter, D. J. and Hargreaves, B. (1986) *A Field Guide to Caterpillars of Butterflies and Moths in Britain and Europe*, Collins, London.

Chinery, M. (1986) *Collins Guide to the Insects of Britain and Western Europe*, Collins, London.

Clark, M. (1988) *Badgers*, Whittet Books, London.

Corbet, G. B. and Southern, H. N. (eds) (1964, 1977) *The Handbook of British Mammals*, Blackwell Scientific Publications, Oxford.

des Forges, G. and Harber, D. D. (1963) *A Guide to the Birds of Sussex*, Oliver and Boyd, Edinburgh.

Fitter, R. and Fitter, A. (1984) *Collins Guide to the Grasses, Sedges, Rushes and Ferns of Britain and Northern Europe*, Collins, London.

Fry, R. and Lonsdale, D. (eds) (1991) *Habitat Conservation for Insects – a Neglected Green Issue*, The Amateur Entomologists' Society, Volume 21, Middlesex.

Goater, B. (1974) *The Butterflies and Moths of Hampshire and the Isle of Wight*, Classey, Faringdon.

Grove, S. and Herbert, G. (1987) *Butterflies of the Southern Chalk Downlands*, British Butterfly Conservation Society.

Hall, P. C. (1980) *Sussex Plant Atlas*, Booth Museum, Brighton.

Heath, J. and Emmett, A. M. (eds) (1976–91) *The Moths and Butterflies of Great Britain and Ireland*, Vols. 1, 7, 9 and 10, Curwen and Harley Books, Colchester, Essex.

Heath, J., Pollard, E. and Thomas, J. A. (1984) *Atlas of Butterflies in Britain and Ireland*, Viking, Harmondsworth, Middlesex.

Herbstein, Denis (1982) *The North Downs Way*, Countryside Commission, HMSO, London.

Homes, R. C. *et al.* (1964) *The Birds of the London Area*, Rupert Hart-Davis, London.

Hudson, W. H. (1923) *Nature in Downland*, Dent, London. Futura Heritage edition 1981, Macdonald Futura, London.

Jennett, Seán (1977) *The South Downs Way*, Countryside Commission. HMSO, London.

Kent Ornithological Society (1990) *The Kent Bird Report for 1988.*

Kent Trust for Nature Conservation leaflets: *Lydden Nature Reserve* (1989), *Park Gate Down Nature Reserve* (1987), *Queendown Warren Nature Reserve* (1987), *Yockletts Bank Nature Reserve* (1988).

Lee, A. (1989) *The Wild Places of Sussex*, Sussex Wildlife Trust.

London Natural History Society: *The London Naturalist* 1946–1990. Journal of the Society. *The London Bird Report* 1946–1990. Journal of the Society.

Lousley, J. E. (1950) *Wild Flowers of Chalk and Limestone*, Collins, London.

McClintock, D. and Fitter, R. S. R. (1956) *The Pocket Guide to Wild Flowers*, Collins, London.

Mabey, Richard. (1972) *Food for Free*, Collins, London.

Manning, S. A. (1974) *The Naturalist in South-east England*, David and Charles, Newton Abbot.

Marshall, Judith A. and Haes, E. C. M. (1988) *Grasshoppers and Allied Insects of Great Britain and Ireland*, Harley Books, Colchester, Essex.

Montier, D. J. (ed.) (1977) *Atlas of Breeding Birds of the London Area*, Batsford, London.

Neal, E. G. (1986) *The Natural History of Badgers*, Croom Helm, London.

Parr, D. (ed.) (1972) *Birds in Surrey 1900–1970*, Batsford, London.

Parslow, John (ed.) (1986) *Birdwatcher's Britain*, Pan Books/Ordnance Survey, London.

Peterson, R., Mountfort, G. and Hollom, P. A. D. (1954) Revised edition, 1966. *A Field Guide to the Birds of Britain and Europe*, Collins, London.

Philip, E. G. (1982) *Atlas of the Kent Flora*, Kent Field Club, Maidstone.

Plant, C. W. (1987) *The Butterflies of the London Area*, London Natural History Society, London.

Prater, T., Taylor, D. and Wheatley, J. (1987) *Where to Watch Birds in Kent, Surrey and Sussex*, Christopher Helm, London.

Pratt, C. R. (1981) *A History of the Butterflies and Moths of Sussex*, Booth Museum, Brighton.

Rayner, R. (1979) *Mushrooms and Toadstools*, Hamlyn Nature Guide, London.

Reader's Digest Association (1984) *Field Guide to the Animals of Britain*, The Reader's Digest Nature Lover's Library, London.

Reader's Digest Association (1981) reprinted with amendments 1987, *Field Guide to the Birds of Britain*, The Reader's Digest Nature Lover's Library, London.

Reader's Digest Association (1984) *Field Guide to the Butterflies and other Insects of Britain*, The Reader's Digest Nature Lover's Library, London.

Reader's Digest Association (1981) reprinted with amendments 1988, *Field Guide to the Trees and Shrubs of Britain*, The Reader's Digest Nature Lover's Library, London.

Reader's Digest Association (1984) *Field Guide to the Water Life of Britain*, The Reader's Digest Nature Lover's Library, London.

Reader's Digest Association (1981) reprinted with amendments 1988, *Field Guide to the Wild Flowers of Britain*, The Reader's Digest Nature Lover's Library, London.

Richards, A. J. (1979) *British Birds: a Field Guide*, David and Charles, Newton Abbot.

Richardson, P. (1985) *Bats*, Whittet Books, London.

Rose, F. (1981) *The Wild Flower Key*, Warne, London.

Shrubb, M. (1979) *The Birds of Sussex: their present status*, Phillimore, Chichester.

Skinner, B. (1984) *Colour Identification Guide to Moths of the British Isles* (Macrolepidoptera), Viking, London.

Snow, Barbara and Snow, D. W. (1988) *Birds and Berries: a study of an ecological reaction*, Poyser, Berkhamsted, Herts.

Southwood, T. R. E. (1963) *Life of the Wayside and Woodland*, Warne, London.

Surrey Bird Club (1990) *Surrey Bird Report for 1989*.

Surrey Wildlife Trust (n.d.) *Nature Reserves*. Surrey W.T., Dorking, Surrey.

Sussex Ornithological Society (1987) *Birds of Sussex 1962–1987*.

Sussex Ornithological Society (1990) *The Sussex Bird Report for 1989*.

Tansley, A. G. (1968, 2nd ed.) *Britain's Green Mantle*, Allen and Unwin, London.

Taylor, D. W., Davenport, D. L. and Flegg, J. J. M. (1981; 2nd ed. 1984) *Birds of Kent*, Meresborough, Meopham, Kent.

Trueman, A. E. (1949) *Geology and Scenery in England and Wales*, Pelican Books, Harmondsworth, Middlesex.

White, Gilbert (1789) *The Natural History of Selborne*.

INDEX

Page numbers in *italics* refer to illlustrations

Aconite, winter *Branthis hyemalis* 162
Adder (viper) *Vipera berus* 29, 49, 50
Admiral, red *Vanessa atalanta* 65, 119, 120, *119*; white *Ladoga camilla* 65
Adur, River, Sussex 18, 51, 88
Agrimony *Agrimonia eupatoria* 48
Alresford Valley and Downs, Hampshire 171
Amberley Wild Brooks, Sussex 90, 91, 169, 180, 182, *116–17*
Anemone, wood *Anemone nemorosa* 39, 40
Angle shades moth *Phlogophora meticulosa* 117, 120, 121, 160, *119*
Ant, *Lasius alienus* 101, 104; red *Myrmica sabuleti* 101, 104; yellow meadow *Lasius flavus* 31, 97, 101
Archangel, yellow *Lamiastrum galeobdolon* 14
Argus, brown *Aricia agestis* 29, 58, 59, 105
Arum, wild *Arum maculatum* 33
Arun, River and Valley, Sussex 18, 21, 51, 88, 90, 108, 114, 142, 168, 169
Arundel Park, Sussex 20, 108, 109, 180
Ash *Fraxinus excelsior* 150, 160
Ashtead Common, Surrey 44

Badger *Meles meles* 31, 34–9, 42, 82, 129, 133, 140, 147, *33, 83, 184*
Banstead Downs (Park Downs) Surrey 175
Barlavington Down and Hanger, Sussex 134, 180, *48–9, 135*
Bartsia, red *Odontites verna* 96
Basil, wild *Clinopodium vulgare* 96, 97
Bat, barbastelle *Barbastella barbastellus* 145; Brandt's *Myotis brandtii* 145; common long-eared *Plecotus auritus* 145;

Daubenton's (water) *Myotis daubentoni* 145; Leisler's *Nycatalus leisleri* 145; Natterer's *Myotis nattereri* 145; pipistrelle *Pipistrellus pipistrellus* 34, 145; serotine *Eptisecus serotinus* 145; whiskered *Myotis mystacinus* 145
Beachy Head, Sussex 12, 46, 54, 79, 85, 93, 115, 125, 132, 168, 177, *132*
Beacon Hill, Sussex 142, *143*
Beauty moth, lilac *Apeira syringaria* 81; pale brindled *Apocheima pilosaria* 33, 161; small brindled *A. hispidaria* 33, 161; willow *Peribatodes rhomboidaria* 81
Bedstraw, heath *Galium saxatile* 93, 94
Bees 34, 40, 55, 71, 79, 96, 98, 102, 120, *119*; bumble 82, 126, 127; solitary *Eucera* sp. 85
Beech *Fagus sylvatica* 10, 14, 20, 29–31, 36, 38, 43, 62, 63, 67, 80, 82, 86–8, 102, 111, 122, 129, 130, 141, 145, 148, 149, 151, 152, *123*
Beet, sea *Beta vulgaris* spp. *maritima* 55
Beetles 26, 35, 40, 51, 77, 148, 161, 165; burying (sexton) *Nicrophorus humator* and *N. vespilloides* 136; carrion *Necrodes littoralis* 136; dung 82; flower 79; ground 27; rose chafer *Cetonia aurata* 65; soldier 71; stag *Lucanus cervus* 80; water 89
Belle moth, straw *Aspitates gilvaria* 58, 106
Bellflower, clustered *Campanula glomerata* 96, 97
Betchworth Hills, Surrey 175
Betsom's Hill, Westerham, Kent 19
Bewl Water, Tunbridge Wells, Kent 19
Bignor Hill, Sussex *152–3*
Bindweed, field *Convolvulus arvensis* 71
Birch *Betula pendula* and *B. pubescens* 20

Bird's nest, yellow *Monotropa hypopitys* 30
Blackberries *see* bramble
Blackbird *Turdus merula* 33, 77, 128, 133, 151, 152, 158, 168
Blackcap *Sylvia atricapilla* 31, 36, 42, 44, 134, *43, 135*
Blackthorn (sloe) *Prunus spinosus* 79, 81, 84, 128, 149, 157, *8*
Bleak *Alburnus alburnus* 89
Blue butterfly, adonis *Lysandra bellargus* 26, 58, 59, 99, 101, 104, *60–1*; chalk-hill *L. coridon* 26, 29, 59, 99, 101, 104, *100*; common *Polyommatus icarus* 29, 58, 59; holly *Celastrina argiolus* 14, 46, 81; small *Cupido minimus* 58, 59, 99, *48–9*
Bluebell *Hyacinthoides non-scripta* 30, 36, 40, 102, *37*
Bookham Common, Surrey 44, 108, 175
Border moth, dotted *Agriopis marginaria* 33, 161
Botley Hill, Surrey 19
Box *Buxus sempervirens* 30, 62
Box Hill, Surrey 26, 45, 62, 63, 86, 87, 97, 125, *64–5*
Boxley (Hill and Wood), Kent 62, 173
Bracken *Pteridium aguilinum* 30, 82
Bramble *Rubus fruticosus* 30, 79, 81, 82, 84, 105, 121, 128, 129, 134, 140, 165, *135*
Brambling *Fringilla montifringilla* 42, 130, 148, 151, 152
Bretherton, R. F. 117, 119
Brimstone butterfly *Gorepteryx rhamni* 29, 34, 46, 58, 65, 80, 175
Brimstone moth *Opisthograptis luteolata* 81
Brindle moth, yellow-barred *Acasis viretata* 81
British Trust for Ornithology (BTO) 45, 79
Brown butterfly, hedge (gatekeeper) *Pyronia tithonus* 79, 80, 96; meadow

Maniola jurtina 29, 65, 79, 89, 94, 96, 101, *100*; wall *Lasiommata megera* 96
Bryony, black *Tamus communis* 162; white *Bryonia dioica* 111, 162
Buckland Hill, Surrey 63
Buckthorn, alder *Frangula alnus* 80; purging (common) *Rhamnus catharticus* 64, 65, 80, 81, 128, 150
Bugle, common *Ajuga reptans* 29
Bugloss, viper's *Echium vulgare* 57, 87
Bullfinch *Pyrrhula pyrrhula* 14, 30, 128, 148, 149
Bullhead (miller's thumb) *Cottus gobio* 88
Bunting, cirl *Emberiza cirlus* 78; corn *E. calandra* 27, 46; reed *E. schoeniclus* 90
Burnet companion moth *Euclidia glyphica* 61, 62
Burnet moth, five spotted *Zygaena trifolii* 58, 62, 98, 106, 107; narrow-bordered five spotted *Z. lonicerae* 58, 62, 98, 106, 107; six spotted *Z. filipendulae* 58, 62, 106, 107
Burnet, salad *Sanguisorba minor* 26, 87, 94, 98, 107
Burnet-saxifrage *Pimpinella saxifraga* 29, 96, 97, 98, 107, *124*
Bush-crickets (*Tettigonlidae*) *43*, 75, 107–9, 121, 122, 129; dark *Pholidoptera griseoaptera* 107; great green *Tettigonia viridissima* 107; long-winged conehead *Conocephasus discolor* 108; oak *Meconama thalissinum* 107; speckled *Leptophyes punctatissima* 108; wart-biter *Decticus verrucivorus* 177
Butser Hill, Hampshire 171
Butterflies 14, 26, 29, 34, 40, 46–9, 55, 58, 62, 65, 67, 71, 79, 80, 87, 94, 96, 98, 99, 102, 106, 115, 139
Butterfly-bush *Buddleia davidii* 115
Buzzard *Buteo buteo* 29, 41, 42, 151, 165, 168, 169

Cabbage, wild sea *Brassica oleracea* 55

Campion, bladder *Silene v. vulgaris* 57, 70; red *S. dioica* 15, 57, 79; white *S. alba* 57, 79

Carpet moth, chalk *Scotopteryx bipunctaria* 58, 106, 107; pretty chalk *Melanthia procellata* 41, 107

Carrot, wild *Daucus carota* 79, 96-8

Castle Hill and Kingston Scarp, Sussex 60, 104, 177

Catchfly, Nottingham *Silene nutans* 56

Celandine, Lesser *Ranunculus ficaria* 33, 38, 39

Centaury, dwarf *Centaurium capitatum* 55

Chaffinch *Fingilla coelebs* 77, 130, 148, 151, 152

Chalk heath 93, 94

Challock Forest, Kent 137, 173

Chanctonbury Ring, Sussex 74

Charlton Forest, Sussex 137

Cherry, wild (gean) *Prunus avium* 149

Chestnut moth *Conistra vaccinii* 34, 120; beaded *Agrochola lychnidis* 120, *119*; dotted *Conistra rubiginea* 120; red *Cerastis rubricosa* 33

Chestnut, sweet *Castanea sativa* 20, 82, 145

Chickweed, common *Stellaria media* 162

Chicory *Cichorium intybus* 124, 162

Chiffchaff *Pylloscopus collybita* 14, 42, 88, 113

Chub *Leuciscus cephalus* 89

Cinnabar moth 48-9

Cinquefoils *Potentilla* spp. 48

Cissbury Hill and Ring, Sussex 38, 45, 46, 153, 168, 180

Clary *Salvia horminoides* 124

Clay, triple-spotted *Xestia ditrapezium* 81

Clover, red *Trifolium pratense* 105; white *T. repens* 59

Coltsfoot *Tussilago farfara* 33, 38

Comma *Polygonia c-album* 34, 120, *119*

Copper, small *Lycaena phlaeas* 58

Coronet moth *Craniophora ligustri* 81; marbled *Hadena confusa* 55-7; varied *H. comota* 69, 70

Countryside Commission (CC) 94

Cowslip *Primula veris* 36, 8, 37

Crane's-bill, meadow *Geranium pratense* 79

Cricket, field *Gryllus campestris* 109; house- *Acheta domesticus* 109

Crimson and gold, common *Pyrausta purpuralis* 61, 62

Crows (corvids) 134, 144 167; carrion *Corvus corone* 29, 42, 133, 151, 153

Crundale Downs, Kent 44, 87, 94, 174

Cuckmere Haven, Sussex 54, 55, 88, 169, 177; River and Valley 18, 20, 51, 168, 169, 179

Cuckoo *Cuculus canorus* 111, 47

Curlew *Numenius arguata* 54, 169

Curlew, stone *Burhinus oedicnemus* 22, 74, 75

Dace *Leuciscus leuciscus* 89

Damselfly, banded demoiselle *Calopteryx splendens* 89; beautiful demoiselle *C. virgo* 89

Dandelion *Taraxacum offcinale* 38, 58, 162

Darent, River and Valley, Kent 18, 44, 46, 51, 87, 88, 173, 89

Darwin, Charles 87, 88, 126

Darwin's Orchid Bank, Downe, Kent 173, *29*

Dawcombe Wood, Surrey 175

Deadnettle, red *Lamium purpureum* 38, 162

December moth *Poecilocamoa pupuli* 155, 160

Deer 129, 133, 136; fallow *Dama dama* 134, 137, 139, *135-6*; muntjac *Muntiacus reevesi* 139, 140; red *Cervus elaphus* 134, 137; roe *Capreolus capreolus* 137, 139, *138*, 140, 174

Delicate moth *Eythimna vitellina* 116

Denbies Hillside, Surrey 176

Devil's Kneading Trough, Wye Down, Kent *90-1*

Ditchling Beacon, Sussex 19, 87, 97, 177, *21*

Dogwood *Cornus sanguinea* 64, 65, 79, 80, 81, 128, 150

Dormouse, common *Muscardinus avellanarius* 129, 140, 144-6, 148, 162

Dove, collared *Streptopelia decaocto* 70, 77, 78; rock *Columba livia* 68; stock *C. oenas* 45, 77, 152, 153; turtle *Streptopelia turtur* 30, 77, *78*, 172

Dover, White Cliffs, Kent 11, 23, 54, 55, 68, 69, 85, 132, 173

Downe (Greater London) 87, 88, 173

Dropwort *Filipendula vulgaris* 40, 94, 96, 99

Duck, eider *Somateria mollissima* 132; tufted *Aythya fuligula* 169

Duncton, Chalk-pit and Hill, Sussex 19, 181

Dunlin *Calidris alpina* 169

Dunnock (hedge sparrow) *Prunella modularis* 77

Early Grey moth *Xylocampa areola* 33

Early moth *Theria primaria* 33, 155, 157

Eel *Anguilla anguilla* 88

Eggar moth, oak *Lasiocampa quercus* 81, 84

Elder *Sambucus nigra* 30, 144

Elm *Ulmus* sp. 160

Emerald moth, light *Campaea margaritata* 81; small *Hamistola chrysoprasaria* 107

Emperor butterfly, purple *Apatura iris* 34

Emperor moth *Saturnia pavonia* 81, 84

English Channel 11, 51, 54, 68, 88, 114, 115, 118

English Nature (EN) 94, 104

Epsom Common and Downs, Surrey 44, 175

Eyebright, common *Euphrasia nemorosa* 29, 96, 104

Falcon, hobby, *see* Hobby falcon; Peregrine *Falco peregrinus* 54, 169, *23*

Fern moth *Horisme tersata* 41

Fescue, mat-grass *Vulpia unilateralis* 94; red *Festuca rubra* 61, 94, 96; sheep's *F. ovina* 10, 61, 94, 96, 105, 106

Fieldfare *Turdus pilaris* 42, 128, 152, 154, 158, *154-5*, *159*

Finches 29, 115, 128, 151, 152, 154, *146-7*

Firecrest *Regulus ignicapillus* 142, *143*

Fish 51, 88, 89

Flax, fairy (purging) *Linum catharticum* 96; linseed *L. usitatissimum* 21

Flies (Diptera) 55, 65, 98, 102, 129, 161, 162; bee- (Bombyliidae) 40; blow- (Calliphoridae) 120, 129; caddis (Trichoptera) 89, 120; drone *Eristalis* spp. 120, *119*; hover- (Syrphidae) 40, 71, 79, 96, 98, 120, *119*; robber (Asilidae) 27; saw- (Hymenoptera: Symphyta) 65, 79

Flycatchers 112, 115; pied *Picedula hypoleuca* 42, 113, 134; spotted *Musciapa striata* 134, 69

Folkestone Warren, Kent 11, 54, 55, 85, 108, 173, 174, *22-3*

Footman moth, orange *Eilema sororcula* 30

Forester moth, cistus *Adscita geryon* 98, 106, 107; common *A. statices* 98, 107; scarce *A. globulariae* 98, 106, 107

Forestry Commission (FC) 20

Fox *Vulpes vulpes* 29, 41, 129, 133, 139, 140, 142, 144, 147, 165-7, *143*

Foxglove *Digitalis purpurea* 93

Friston Forest, Sussex 20, 45, 169, 178

Fritillary butterfly, dark green *Mesoacidalia aglaia* 105, *23*; Duke of Burgundy *Hamearis lucina* 48-9

Frog, common *Rana temporaria* 50, 164, 165

Fulking, Sussex 94-5, *126-7*

Fulmar petrel *Fulmarus glacialis* 54, 57, *56-7*

Fumitory, common *Fumaris officinalis* 71, 77

Fungi 82, 122, 130, 131, 133, 141, *123*

Gall, pea *Diplolepis eglanterine* 161; Robin's pincushion (bedeguar) *D. rosae* 142, 161, *143*; spiked pea *D. nervosus* 161

Gannet *Sula bassana* 132, *132*

Garlic, mustard *Alliaria petiolata* 14, 49; wild *Allium ursinum, see* Ramsons

Gem moth *Orthonama obstipata* 116; Stephen's *Autographa biloba* 118

Gentian, autumn (felwort) *Gentianella amarella* 88, 105, 124, 125, 134, *135*

Geometridae (geometer moths) 33, 34, 62, 156, 157

Glow worm *Lampyris noctiluca* 70

Gnat, winter *Trichocers* sp. 161

Goldcrest *Regulus regulus* 142, 151, *143*

Goldfinch *Carduelis carduelis* 77, 98

Goosander *Mergus merganser* 169

Goose *Ulex europaeus* 93; brent *Branta bernicla* 169; Canada *B. canadensis* 169; grey lag *Anser anser* 169; white-fronted *A. albifrons* 91, 169

Grass, annual meadow- *Poa annua* 61, 120; bent *Agrostis* spp. 96; cock's foot *Dactylis glomerata* 96, 120; common couch *Elymus repens* 96; crested dog's tail *Cynosurus cristatus* 96; crested hair *Koeleria macrantha* 40, 94; downy oat- *Avenula pubescens* 94; false brome- *Brachyposium sylvaticum* 96; false-oat *Arrhenatherum elatius* 96; fern *Desmazeria rigida* 96; meadow- *Poa* spp. 96; meadow oat- *Avenula pratensis* 40; narrow-leaved meadow- *Poa angustifolia* 94; quaking *Briza media* 96; sweet vernal- *Anthoxanthum odoratum* 96; Timothy *Phleum pratense* 96; tor *Brachypodium pinnatum* 40, 94; upright brome- *Bromus erectus* 40, 94; yellow-oat

Trisetum flavescens 94; Yorkshire fog *Holcus lanatus* 96, 120

Grasshoppers (*Acrididae*) 26, 27, 43, 51, 67, 75, 107–9; common green *Omocestus viridulus* 108; field *Chorthippus brunneus* 108; meadow *C. parallelus* 108; mottled *Myrmeleotettix maculatus* 108; stripe-winged *Stenobothrus lineatus* 108; woodland *Omocestus rufipes* 108

Grayling butterfly *Hipparchia semele* 94, 96, 105, 106

Grebe, little *Podiceps ruficollis* 90

Greenfinch *Carduelis chloris* 77, 152

Greenshank *Tringa nebularia* 169

Groundhopper, common *Tetrix undulata* 108

Groundsel *Senecio vulgaris* 162

Gudgeon *Gobio gobio* 89

Guillemot *Uria aalge* 54

Gull, black-headed *Larus ridibundus* 152, 153; common *L. canus* 152; great black-backed *L. marinus* 169; herring *L. argentatus* 54, 68; lesser black-backed *L. fuscus* 54, 68, 169

Hairstreak butterflies 65; brown *Thecla batulae* 81; green *Callophrys rubi* 29, 58, 81, *48–9*

Hampshire and Isle of Wight Naturalists' Trust (HWT) 104

Hampshire Downs 84, 105, 108

Hanging Wood, Caterham, Surrey 63

Hare, brown *Lepus capensis* 29, 41, 52, 53, 162, 164, 168, *163*

Harrier, hen *Circus cyaneus* 29, 168, 169, *166–7*

Hawfinch *Coccothraustes coccothraustes* 149, 150

Hawk, sparrow *Accipiter nisus* 29, 30, 51, 54, 151, 168, 169, *166–7*

Hawk-moth, bedstraw *Hyles gallii* 16, 118; convolvulus *Agrius convolvuli* 116; death's head *Acherontia atropos* 116; eyed *Smerinthus ocellata* 34; humming bird *Macroglossum stellatarum* 160; poplar *Laothoe populi* 34; privet *Sphinx ligustri* 81; silver-striped *Hippotion celerio* 116; small elephant *Deilephila porcellus* 107

Hawk's-beard *Crepis* spp. 107

Hawkweed *Hieracium* spp. 58, 105, 107, 162

Hawthorn (haws) *Crategus monogyna* 29, 67, 79, 81, 84, 111, 114, 128, 141, 149, 154, 157, 158, 160, 162, *159*

Hazel *Corylus avellana* 30, 36, 82, 129, 134, 145, 162, *37*

Heath butterfly, small *Coenonympha pamphilus* 29, 58, 60, 96

Heath moth, latticed *Semiothisa clathrata* 61, 62

Heather (Ling) *Calluna vulgaris* 81, 93, 94; bell *Erica cinerea* 94

Heaths *Erica* spp. 93

Hebrew character moth *Orthosia gothica* 33

Hedgehog *Erinaceus europaeus* 27, 82, 140, 141, 144, 147, 148, 165

Heliotrope, winter *Petasites fragrans* 162

Hellebore, stinking *Helleborus foetidus* 30, 33, 38, 40, 88, 162, *39*

Helleborine, broad-leaved (common *Epipactis helleborine* 86; narrow-lipped *E. leptochila* 86; violet *E. purpurata* 84, 86; white *Cephalanthera damsonium* 86

Henbane *Hyoscamus niger* 72, 73

Herald moth *Scoliopteryx libatrix* 34, 120, 119

Herb Paris *Paris quadrifolia* 40

Heron, grey *Ardea cinerea* 144, 151

Hobby falcon *Falco subbuteo* 51, 54, 112, *5, 27*

Hog's Back, Surrey 11, 12, 19, 44, 108, 125, 139, 176, *146–7*

Hogweed *Heracleum sphondylium* 79

Holly *Ilex aguifolium* 30, 81, 128, 150, 162

Honeydew 46, 59

Honeysuckle, common *Lonicera periclymenum* 30, 79, 81, 146

Hook-tip moth, barred *Drepana cultraria* 30

Hop *Humulus lupulus* 22

Hornbeam *Carpinus betulus* 20, 149

Howell Hill, Surrey 176

Hudson, W. H. 9, 21, 36, 74, 114

Itchen, River, Hampshire 13, 172

Ivy *Hedera helix* 81, 114, 120, 140, *118, 119*

Jack-by-the-hedge, *see* garlic mustard

Jackdaw *Corvus monedula* 27, 45, 54, 55, 77, 152

Jay *Garrulus glandarius* 130, 134, 139, 148, 151, *135*

Juniper *Juniperus communis* 63, 128

Kent Trust for Nature Conservation (KTNC) 87, 104

Kestrel *Falco tinnunculus* 29, 51, 54, 68, 69, 111, 144, 165, 167, 168, 169, *110, 166–7*

Kingfisher *Alcedo atthis* 90

Kingley Vale, Sussex 45, 63, 108, 137, 139, 150, 151, 181, *138, 150*

Kitten moth, sallow *Furcula furcula* 34

Kittiwake *Risa tridactyla* 54, 68, 69, 132

Knapweeds 58, 104–7; black (lesser) *Centaurea nigra* 96, 107, 124; greater *C. scabiosa* 96, 107

Lackey moth *Malacosoma neustria* 81, 84

Lady's smock *Cardamine pratensis* 49

Lady's-tresses, autumn *Spiranthes spiralis* 102, 124–6, *103*

Lampern *Lampetra fluviatilis* 88

Lamprey, brook *Lampetra planeri* 88

Lappet moth *Gastropacha guercifolia* 84

Lapwing *Vanellus vanellus* 24, 92, 133, 152, 153, 169, *25, 116–17, 146–7*

Larch *Larix decidua* 20

Larks 115, 168, *4, 146–7*

Levin Down, Sussex 94, 181

Linch Down, Bepton, Sussex 19

Ling (heather) *see* heather

Linnet *Carduelis cannabina* 30, 77, 79, 98, 152, *146–7*

Lizards 27, 49–51, 75, 106, 164; common *Lacerta vivipara* 27, 49, 51

Loach, stone *Noemacheilus barbatulus* 89

Lobster moth *Stauropus fabi* 30

Lousley, J. E. 16, 26, 96, 125

Lucerne *Medicago sativa* 21, 62, 71

Lullington Heath, Sussex 94, 168, *154–5*

Lychpole Hill, Sussex 46, 134, 180, *135, 166–7*

Lydden and Stonewall, Kent 104, 173

Lyminge (and Forest), Kent 174

Mabey, Richard 96

Magpie *Pica pica* 77, 133, 134, 151–3, 165, *64–5*

Magpie Bottom, Shoreham, Kent 173, *92–3*

Magpie moth *Abraxas grossulariata* 81

Mallard *Anas platyrhynchos* 54, 92

Malling Down, Sussex 104, 178, *130–1*

Mallows *Malva* spp. 79

Maple, field *Acer campestra* 29, 64, 65, 80, 84, 149, 150

March moth *Alsophila aesculria* 33, 155, 161

Marjoram *Origanum vulgare* 29, 87, 96, 104, 105, 124, *100–1*

Martin, house *Delichon urbica* 55, 69, 88, 111, 112, *4, 112–3*; sand *Riparia riparia* 111, 112

Mayfly (Green Drake) *Ephemera danica* 89

Meadowsweet *Filipendula ulmaria* 99

Medway, River, Kent 18, 19, 51, 88

Mercury, dog's *Mercurialis perennis* 30, 33, 38, 40

Merlin *Falco columbarius* 29, 168, 169

Mice 77, 165, 166; harvest *Micromys minutus* 129, 141, 144; wood (long-tailed field) *Apodemus sylvaticus* 31, 129, 133, 141, 145, 151, 157, 158, 162, 129; yellow-necked *A. flavicollis* 141, 144

Milkwort, chalk *Polygala calcarea* 57, 58; common *P. vulgaris* 57, 58, 61; Kentish *P. amarella* 58

Mill Hill, Shoreham-bySea, Sussex 181, *60–1*

Minnow *Phoxinum phoxinus* 89

Mocha moth *Cyclophora annuleta* 84

Mole *Talpa europaea* 27

Mole, River, Surrey 18, 51, 62, 88

Monarch butterfly *Danaus plexippus* 115, 118

Mother Shipton moth *Callistege mi* 61, 62

Moths 30, 31, 34, 58, 62, 67, 77, 80, 81, 84, 87, 99, 102, 106, 107, 115, 116, 155

Mount Caburn, Lewes, Sussex 179

Mouse, *see* mice

Mouse-ear, field *Cerastium arvense* 73

Mullein, common *Verbascus thapsus* 97; dark *V. nigrum* 40, 96, 97; white *V. lychnitis* 87

Mushrooms 130; common parasol *Lepiota procera* 122; shaggy parasol *L. rhacodes* 122, *123*

Myxomatosis 41, 59, 106, 125, 165

National Trust (NT) 14, 62, 94, 105

Nature Conservancy Council (NCC) 94

Nightingale *Luscinia megarhyncha* 30, 36, 42, 44, 88, 112, *37*

Nightshade, deadly (belladonna) *Atropa belladonna* 71, 124, 128

Noctuidae (owlet moths) 33, 34, 56, 58, 66

Norbury Park, Surrey 176

North Downs Way 23, 63

North Foreland, Broadstairs, Kent 79, 132

North Sea 19, 115, 118

November moth *Epirrita dilutata* 155, 156

Nuthatch *Sitta europaea* 14, 31, 45, 88, 129, 139, 148, 151, *149*

Oak, common (pedunculate) *Quercus robur* 10, 20, 30, 31, 36, 40, 43, 67, 84, 134, 150, 152, 156, 160

Oak moth, scalloped *Crocallis elinguaria* 81

Old man's beard *see* traveller's joy

Old Winchester Hill, Hampshire 60, 104, 108, 172, *112–13*

Orange moth *Angerona prunaria* 81

Orange tip butterfly *Anthocharis cardamines* 14, 46, 48, 58

Orchids 125; bee *Ophrys apifera* 85, 87, 102, *103*; bird's-nest *Neottia nidus-avis* 30, 86, 88; burnt *Orchis ustulata* 85, 87; common spotted *Dactylorhiza fuchsii* 29, 87, 102, *103*; early purple *Orchis mascula* 86, 102, *103*; early spider *Ophrys sphegodes* 84, 85, 87; fly *O. insectifera* 29, 86, 87, 102, *103*; fragrant (sweet-scented) *Gymnadenia conopsea* 29, 87, 102, *92–3*, *103*; frog *Coeloglossum viride* 87, 102, *103*; greater butterfly *Platanthera chlorantha* 86, 87, 102, *103*; green-winged (green-veined) *Orchis morio* 87; lady *O. purpurea* 84, 86, 87; late spider *Ophrys fuciflora* 85–7; lesser butterfly *Platanthera bifolia* 86, 87; man *Aceras anthropophorum* 29, 85–7; monkey *Orchis simia* 84, 86; musk *Herminium monorchis* 84, 87; pyramidal *Anacamptis pyramidalis* 29, 87, 102, 105, *103*

Ouse, River, Sussex 18, 51, 88

Ouzel, ring *Turdus torquatus* 42, 113–5, 128, *13*, *114*

Owls 144, 157, 165; barn *Tyto alba* 67, *66*; little *Athene noctua* 29, 76, 77; long-eared *Asio otus* 151, *31*; short-eared *A. flammeus* 29, 169; tawny *Strix aluco* 31, 151

Painted lady butterfly *Cynthia cardui* 99, 115; American *C. virginiensis* 118

Park Gate Down, Elham, Kent 174

Parsnip, wild *Pastinaca sativa* 71, 96, 97

Partridge, chukar *Alectoria chukar* 76; grey *Perdix perdix* 24, 74, 75, 152, *25*, *146–7*; red-legged (French) *Alectoris rufa* 24, 27, 74, 75, 152, *25*; rock *A. graeca* 76

Peacock butterfly *Inachis io* 34, 65, 120

Perch *Perca fluviatilis* 89

Pesticides 54, 75, 145

Pheasant *Phasianus colchicus* 148, 152, 153

Pigeon, feral *Columba livia* 54, 55, 68, 69; wood *C. palumbus* 77, 151–3

Pike *Esox lucius* 89

Pilgrims' Way 23

Pine, ground- *Ajuga champaepitys* 73, 74

Pine, Scots *Pinus sylvestris* 20, 30

Pinion moth, tawny *Lithopane semibrunnea* 34, 120

Pintail *Anas acuta* 91, 169

Pipits 115, 168; meadow *Anthus pratensis* 27, 29, 55, 152, 154; rock *A. Spinoletta petrosus* 55, 68, *56–7*; tree *A. trivialis* 30, 44, 55, 112

Plantain, hoary *Plantago media* 96

Plover, golden *Pluvialis apricaria* 152, 153, 169; grey *P. squatarola* 169; ringed *Charadrius hiaticula* 169

Pochard *Aythya ferina* 91, 92, 169

Polesden Lacey, Dorking, Surrey 176

Poplar *Populus* sp. 160

Poppy, common (corn, field) 71; yellow horned- *Glaucium flavum* 55

Primrose *Primula vulgaris* 33, 39

Privet, wild *Ligustrum vulgaris* 64, 65, 79, 80, 81, 105

Prominent moth, maple *Ptilodontella cucullina* 84; plumed *Ptilophora plumigera* 84, 160

Puffin *Fratercula arctica* 132

Pug moth, maple *Eupithecia inturbata* 84; pimpinel *E. pimpinellata* 107

Pulborough Brooks, Sussex 91, 168, 169, 182

Purbeck, Isle of, Dorset 11, 85, 108

Purple-barred moth, small *Phytometra viridaria* 81

Puss moth *Cerura vinuula* 34

Quail *Coturnix coturnix* 76

Quaker moth, powdered *Orthosia gracilis* 33; red-line *Agrochola lota* 120, *119*; small *Orthosia cruda* 33; twin-spotted *O. munda* 33

Queen Elizabeth Country Park, Hampshire 171

Queen Elizabeth Forest Park and War Down, Hampshire 172

Queendown Warren, Kent 104, 174

Rabbit *Oryctolagus cuniculus* 10, 29, 41, 42, 59, 72, 75, 82, 85, 94, 101, 105, 106, 125–7, 162, 165, 168, *95*, *126–7*

Ragwort, common *Senecio jacobaea* 124; hoary *S. erucifolius* 29, 124

Rampion, round-headed *Phyteuma tenerum* 97

Ramsons *Allium ursinum* 40

Ranmore Common, Surrey 63, 176

Rape, oilseed *Brassica napus* 21, 79

Rats 50, 133, 164, 165

Redshank *Tringa totanus* 90, 92, 169

Redstart *Phoenicurus phoenicurus* 42, 45, 112, 134, *112–3*, *135*; black *P. obscurus* 68

Redwing *Turdus iliacus* 42, 128, 152, 154, 158, *154–5*, *159*

Reigate and Colley Hills, Surrey 45, *104*, 175, 176

Restharrow (common) *Ononis repens* 59

Ringlet butterfly *Aphantopus hyperantus* 29, 80

Roach *Rutilus rutilus* 89

Robin *Erithacus rubecula* 14, 31, 33, 45, 128, 133

Rock-rose, common *Helianthemum nummularium* 26, 40, 58, 59, 96, 99, 107

Rook *Corvus frugilegus* 33, 77, 152, *11*, *182*

Rose, dog *Rosa canina* 79, 111, 128, 142, 161, 162, *143*

Rowan *Sorbus aucuparia* 82, 128

Royal mantle moth *Catarhoe cuculata* 107, 120

Royal Society for the Protection of Birds (RSPB) 169

Ruff *Philomachus pugnax* 169

Rush veneer moth *Nomophila noctuella* 116

Rustic moth, rosy *Hydraecia minacea* 120

Rye Harbour, Sussex 36

Saddlescombe and Chalk-pit, Sussex 182

Sainfoin *Onobrychis viciifolia* 71

Saint Catherine's Hill, Winchester, Hampshire 172

Salisbury Plain, Wiltshire 9, 11, 107

Sallow *Salix* spp. 34, 84; great *S. caprea* 34

Sallow moth *Xanthia icteritia* 120; barred *X. aurago* 30, 84, 120; centre-barred *Athethmia centrago* 120, *119*; pink-barred *Xanthia togata* 120, *119*

Samphire, rock *Crithmum maritimum* 55

Sanicle *Sanicula europaea* 30, 40

Satellite moth *Eupsilia transversa* 34 84, 120

Scabious, field *Knautia arvensis* 96, 99, 105, 106, 124;

small *Scabiosa columbaria* 29, 40, 96, 99, 105, 124

Seaford (and Head), Sussex 93, 94, 125, 168, 178, 179

Seale Chalk-pit, Hog's Back, Surrey 176

Selborne Common and Hanger, Hampshire 13, 14, 16, 30, 38, 43, 44, 63, 74, 86, 88, 108, 109, 172, *124–5*

Seven Sisters cliffs, Sussex 132

Seven Sisters Country Park, Sussex 169, 179

Shakespeare Cliff, Dover, Kent 68, 132

Shelduck *Tadorna tadorna* 92, 169

Shepherd's purse *Capsella bursa-pastoris* 71

Shoulder-knot moth, grey *Lithophane ornitopus* 34, 120

Shoveler *Anas clypeata* 91, 169

Shrews 133, 139, 141, 157; common *Sorex areaneus* 27, 144; pygmy *S. minutus* 27, 144; water *Meomys fodiens* 144

Silver-lines moth, green *Pseudoips fagana* 30

Silver y moth *Autographa gamma* 116, 119, 120, 134, *119*, *135*; scarce *Syngrapha interrogationis* 116

Silverweed *Potentilla anserina* 48, 87

Skipper butterfly, dingy *Erynnis tages* 58, 62, *48–9*; Essex *Thymelicus lineola* 94; grizzled *Pyrgus malvae* 46–8, *48–9*; large *Ocholdes venatus* 94, 101, 104, *100*; silver-spotted *Hesperia comma* 96, 98, 104, 105

Skua, great *Stercorarius skua* 132; pomarine *S. pomarinus* 132

Skylark *Alauda arvensis* 27, 29, 45, 46, 152, 154, 76, *146–7*

Slindon Forest, Sussex 137

Slow worm *Anguis fragilis* 50

Snake, grass *Natrix natrix* 49–51

Snipe *Gallinago gallinago* 90, 92, 169, *116–7*; jack *Lymnocryptes minimus* 169

Snout moth, buttoned *Hypena rostralis* 120

Snowdrop *Galanthus nivalis* 162

Sorrels *Rumex* spp. 107; wood- *Oxalis acetosella* 30, 40

South Downs Way 23, 90, 142

South Foreland, Kent 11, 79, 132

Sparrows 29, 152; house *Passer domesticus* 51, 69, 77

Speckled wood *Parage aegeria* 14, 29, 46, 47, 58

Speedwell, field *Veronica persica* 38, 162

Spiders 50, 121, 124, 142, 148

Spikenard, ploughman's *Inula conyza* 29

Spindle *Euonymus europaeus* 29, 64, 65, 80, 81, 94, 111, 128, 151, 162

Spring usher moth *Agripis leucophaearia* 33, 155, 161

Spurge-laurel *Daphne laureola* 30, 38–40, 88, 162

Squinancywort *Asperula cynchica* 87, 96, 97

Squirrel, grey *Sciurus carolinensis* 129, 134, 139–41, 162, 165, *135*; red *S. vulgaris* 129

Starling *Sturnus vulgaris* 27, 69, 77, 152–4

Stickleback, three-spined *Casterosteus aculeatus* 88

Stitchwort, greater *Stellaria holostea* 39, 73

Stota *Mustela examinea* 29, 35, 41, 42, 144, 164, 165, *164*

Stonechat *Saxicola torquata* 27

Stonefly 89

Stork's-bill, hemlock (common) *Brodium cicutarium* 59

Straw moth, dark bordered *Heliothus peltigera* 116; scarce bordered *H. armigera* 116

Strawberry, wild *Fragaria vesca* 48

Stour River, Great, Kent 18, 51, 88

Surrey Wildlife Trust (SWT) 104

Sussex Wildlife Trust (SXWT) 91, 94, 104, 169

Swallow *Hirundo rustica* 27, 42, 51, 88, 111, 112, 115, *4, 60–1, 112–3*

Swallow-tailed moth *Ourapteryx sambucaria* 81

Swan, Bewick's *Cygnus columbianus* 91, 92, 169; mute *C. olor* 169

Sweet-briar *Rosa rubiginosa* 79

Sweet-william *Dianthus barbatus* 69, 70

Swift *Apus apus* 51, 88, 111

Sword-grass moth, dark *Xylena exsoleta* 116

Teal *Anas crecca* 91, 92, 169

Telscombe Cliffs, Sussex 108

Temple Ewell Downs, near Dover, Kent 174

Thames, River 11, 18, 19, 88

Thanet, Isle of, Kent 11, 132

Thistles 77, 104–7; Carline *Carlina vulgaris* 105, 124, 127, 128; dwarf (stemless) *Cirsium acaule* 96, 98, 105; musk (nodding) *Carduus nutans* 96,

98, 124; seaside (slender) *C. tenuiflorus* 55

Thorn moth, early *Selenia dentaria* 81; August *Ennomos quercinaria* 30

Thrushes 29, 149, 161; mistle *Turdus viscivorus* 128, 152, 158; song *T. philomelos* 33, 77, 128, 152, 158, *159*

Thyme, wild *Thymus drucei* 26, 61, 96, 97, 107

Tits 31, 139, 148, 157; blue *Parus caeruleus* 130, 151; coal *P. ater* 151; great *P. major* 130, 133, 151, 152; long-tailed *Aegithalos caudatus* 131, 142, 151, *130–1, 143*; marsh *Parus palustris* 14, 151

Toad, common *Bufo bufo* 27, 50

Toadflax, yellow (common) *Linaria vulgaris* 79, 124

Toadstools 130; beechwood sickener *Russula mairei* 122, 123; bitter brittle-gill (geranium-scented russula) *R. fellea* 122, *123*; death cap *Amanita phalloides* 131; magpie ink cap *Coprinus picaceus* 122, *123*; panther cap *Amanita pantherina* 122, 131, *123*; red-staining inocybe *Inocybe patouillardii* 122, *123*; *Tricholoma argyraceum* 122, *123*

Tortoiseshell butterfly, small *Aglais urticae* 34, 46, 58

Traveller's joy (old man's beard) *Clematis vitalba* 40, 41, 79, 107, 128, 139, 162, *138*

Treecreeper *Certhia familiaris* 151, 157

Trefoil, bird's-foot *Lotus corniculatus* 29, 58, 59, 107, 124, *92–3*; greater *L. uliginoeus* 107

Tresses, autumn lady's- *Spiranthes spiralis* 87, 124, 125

Trout, brown *Salmo trutta* 88, 172; rainbow *S. gairdneri* 89

Turner, William 55

Twayblade, common *Listera ovata* 29, 86, 87, 102, *103*

Umber moth, dark *Philereme transversata* 81; mottled *Erannis defoliaria* 156; scarce *Agriopis aurantiaria* 156; small waved *Horisme vitalbata* 41; waved *Mepophora abruptaria* 81

Underwing moth, common (large) *Noctus pronuba* 116, 117;

lunar *Omphaloscelis lunosa* 120, *119*; orange *Archiearis parthenias* 33; pearly *Peridroma saucia* 116, 160

Upperwing moth, beautiful *Utetheisa bella* 118

Valerian, red *Centranthus ruber* 57

Vestal moth *Rhodonetra sacraria* 116

Vetch, horseshoe *Hippocrepis comosa* 26, 29, 58, 96, 99, 101, 104; kidney *Anthyllis vulneraria* 29, 40, 58, 59, 96, 99; tufted *Vicia cracca* 79

Violet, common dog- *Viola riviniana* 36, 40, 105; hairy *V. hirta* 29, 40, 87, 105; sweet *V. odorata* 33, 36, 37

Voles 51, 77, 133, 165, 166, 168; bank *Clethrionomys glareolus* 129, 141, 144, 145, 158; short-tailed field *Microtus agrestis* 29, 129, 141, 144

Wagtail, pied *Motacilla alba* 152, 154; yellow *M. flava* 90, 92

Waltham Brooks, Sussex 91, 169, 182

Walton Downs, Surrey 175

Warblers 112, 115, 134, 142; garden *Sylvia borin* 30, 36, 42; grasshopper *Locustella naeria* 27, 29, 42–4, 44; sedge *Acrocephalus schoenobaenus* 90; willow *Phylloscopus trochilus* 14, 30, 42, 88, 113; wood *P. sibilatrix* 14, 31, 42, 43, 88

Wasps 34, 79, 82, 86, 98, 120, 129, *119*; hunting 27; ichneumon- 71; sphecid *Gorytes campestris* 85; sphecid *G. mystaceus* 85

Wayfaring tree *Viburnum lantana* 40, 64, 79, 128, *64–5*

Weald 10, 17–19, 88, 153

Weasel *Mustela nivalis* 29, 41, 50, 144, 164, 165

Weevil, hazel nut *Curculio nucum* 129; oak nut *C. villosus* 129

West Burton Hill, Sussex 152–3

West Dean Woods, Sussex 182

Wey, River, Surrey 18, 19, 51, 88

Wheatear *Oenanthe oenanthe* 27, 36, 42, 74, 113, 114, *37, 72–3*

Whinchat *Saxicola rubetra* 27, 30

White butterfly, green-veined *Pieris napi* 46, 48, 58; large *P.*

brassicae 46, 115; marbled *Melanargia galathea* 94, 96, 105, *21*; small *Pieris rapae* 46, 48, 115

White, Gilbert 13, 14, 43, 44, 63, 74, 86, 88, 109, 114, 125

White moth, broad-barred *Hecatera bicolorata* 107

White-point moth *Mythimna albipuncta* 116

White-speck moth *Mythimna unipuncta* 116

White spot moth *Hadena albimacula* 55, 56

Whitebeam *Sorbus aria* 64, 65, 79, 111, 128, 162

Whitethroat *Sylvia communis* 30, 42, 77, 78; lesser *S. curruca* 14, 42, 77–9, 134, *135*

Wigeon *Anas penelope* 91, 92, 169

Willow, goat *Salix caprea* 34; pussy *S. caprea* 34

Wilmington, Long Man of *72–3*

Windover Hill, Sussex *154–5*

Winnall Moors, Winchester, Hampshire 172

Winter moth *Operophtera brumata* 156; northern *O. fagata* 156

Woodcock *Scolopax rusticola* 31, 151, *17, 157*

Woodlark *Lullula arborea* 45, 46

Woodpecker, great spotted *Dendrocopus major* 14, 31, 45, 129, 149, 151; green *Picus viridis* 14, 27, 31, 45, 88, *179*; lesser spotted *Dendrocopus minor* 31, 45, 151

Woodruff *Galium odoratum* 14, 30, 40

Wort, St. John's *Hypericum* spp. 79

Wren *Troglodytes troglodytes* 77

Wye Downs, Kent 44, 48, 87, 94, 108, 174, *90–1*

Yellow butterfly, clouded *Colias crocea* 71, 115; pale clouded *C. hyale* 71

Yellowhammer *Emberiza citrinella* 27, 30, 46, 67, 77, 78, *146–7*

Yellow horned moth *Achlya flavicornis* 33

Yellow-wort *Blackstonia perfoliata* 40, 87, 96, 98

Yew *Taxus baccata* 30, 63, 82, 87, 111, 114, 128, 149–51, 162, *110, 150*

Yockletts Bank, Kent 174

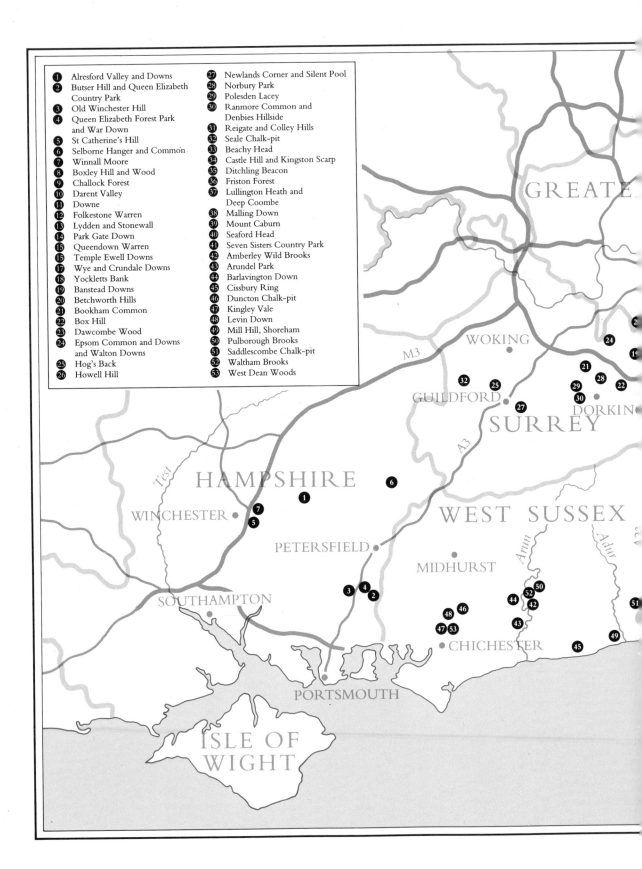

❶	Alresford Valley and Downs	㉗	Newlands Corner and Silent Pool
❷	Butser Hill and Queen Elizabeth Country Park	㉘	Norbury Park
❸	Old Winchester Hill	㉙	Polesden Lacey
❹	Queen Elizabeth Forest Park and War Down	㉚	Ranmore Common and Denbies Hillside
❺	St Catherine's Hill	㉛	Reigate and Colley Hills
❻	Selborne Hanger and Common	㉜	Seale Chalk-pit
❼	Winnall Moore	㉝	Beachy Head
❽	Boxley Hill and Wood	㉞	Castle Hill and Kingston Scarp
❾	Challock Forest	㉟	Ditchling Beacon
❿	Darent Valley	㊱	Friston Forest
⓫	Downe	㊲	Lullington Heath and Deep Coombe
⓬	Folkestone Warren	㊳	Malling Down
⓭	Lydden and Stonewall	㊴	Mount Caburn
⓮	Park Gate Down	㊵	Seaford Head
⓯	Queendown Warren	㊶	Seven Sisters Country Park
⓰	Temple Ewell Downs	㊷	Amberley Wild Brooks
⓱	Wye and Crundale Downs	㊸	Arundel Park
⓲	Yockletts Bank	㊹	Barlavington Down
⓳	Banstead Downs	㊺	Cissbury Ring
⓴	Betchworth Hills	㊻	Duncton Chalk-pit
㉑	Bookham Common	㊼	Kingley Vale
㉒	Box Hill	㊽	Levin Down
㉓	Dawcombe Wood	㊾	Mill Hill, Shoreham
㉔	Epsom Common and Downs and Walton Downs	㊿	Pulborough Brooks
㉕	Hog's Back	51	Saddlescombe Chalk-pit
㉖	Howell Hill	52	Waltham Brooks
		53	West Dean Woods

GREATE

WOKING

GUILDFORD

SURREY

DORKIN

M3

A3

HAMPSHIRE

WINCHESTER

Test

PETERSFIELD

WEST SUSSEX

MIDHURST

Arun

Adur

SOUTHAMPTON

CHICHESTER

PORTSMOUTH

ISLE OF WIGHT